MORE Prefixes and Suffixes
Teaching Vocabulary to Improve Reading Comprehension

Written by
Trisha Callella

Editor: Amy Lubben
Designer/Production: Cari Helstrom
Illustrator: Corbin Hillam
Cover Designer: Carlie Hayashi
Art Director: Moonhee Pak
Project Director: Betsy Morris

Table of Contents

Introduction

Many students are good "decoders"—they know how to read a word by sounding out its parts. But often their comprehension of the word's meaning is not as strong. Vocabulary knowledge is an important part of reading comprehension. Research has shown that actively involving students in learning word meanings improves students' comprehension. In fact, improved vocabulary strengthens all areas of literacy—listening, speaking, reading, and writing.

Since increasing and developing students' vocabulary will improve their overall literacy skills and reading comprehension, research recommends teaching students the parts of words. Over half of all English words contain prefixes or suffixes. These affixes provide essential clues to the core meaning of the words students read. Too often, students skip words they do not know as they are reading, which reduces their understanding of the text. For this reason, students need to learn how to break down the meaningful parts of unknown words.

As early as second grade, some state standards require that students begin to use their knowledge of roots, prefixes, and suffixes to determine the meanings of words. *More Prefixes and Suffixes* follows the same easy-to-use format as *Prefixes and Suffixes*. This new resource introduces students to 37 new prefixes and/or suffixes to support their growing vocabulary by teaching them how to "dissect" words and comprehend multisyllabic words, not just decode them. The activities in this resource incorporate all levels of literacy to maximize the transfer of vocabulary into your students' speech, writing, and reading comprehension.

Each lesson has five activity pages to teach students new vocabulary and thereby improve their comprehension skills:

- A take-home **Word List** with parts of speech to study

- A set of hands-on **Vocabulary Sort** cards to match up for independent practice

- An **Application and Practice** page with vocabulary matching or sentence fill-ins and a crossword puzzle

- A set of **Read-Around Review** game cards for small-group review and application

- A **Vocabulary Quiz** using test-prep and fill-in-the-blank formats to assess and extend students' learning

Getting Started

Planning and Scheduling

Review is a critical component to any learning process. Through repetition and practice, your students will begin to recognize the similarities of words that share a common prefix or suffix. They will use the understanding gained from the exercises in this book to "dissect" new words and infer their meanings. They will begin to naturally identify these prefixes and suffixes as they encounter them in their daily reading assignments, and build a broader vocabulary by adopting words that include them. You will reap the rewards of your efforts when you recognize that your students have started to use their new vocabulary words in their oral language and writing assignments. The key to this achievement is consistently incorporating review of these words in your everyday curriculum. This can be done by modeling the use of these words for your students as well as actively acknowledging any students who use these words throughout the day. In addition, games, quizzes, and review activities encourage your students to use these words frequently and incorporate them into their daily conversations.

Adopt the motto "New, New, Review" in your classroom. Because this motto is key to the success of building vocabulary that will transfer to all areas of literacy, *More Prefixes and Suffixes* has been designed to support this structure. After every two prefix and/or suffix lessons, there is a review test. This serves as an easy reminder that ongoing review opportunities are critical to the transfer of learning.

Teach one group of prefixes or suffixes each week, which will establish a three-week teaching cycle. For example, you would teach a new prefix group in week one, a new prefix group in week two, and review the two prefix groups during week three. The review tests included in this book for each pair of prefix or suffix groupings will make this schedule easy to follow. Read the information on pages 5 and 6 for directions on how to implement each lesson. Use the following Suggested Weekly Plan to help you organize and plan your teaching of prefixes and suffixes and new vocabulary.

Suggested Weekly Plan

Day 1: **Introduce vocabulary** in a pocket chart, on an overhead, or on the board.
Play a **game** with the new words (see page 6).
Pass out **Word Lists** to students.

Day 2: **Review vocabulary.**
Play **Vocabulary Sort.**

Day 3: **Review vocabulary.**
Have students complete the **Application and Practice** page.
Use the **Read-Around Review** game cards with small groups.

Day 4: **Review vocabulary.**
Play a **game** with the vocabulary words.
Optional: Have students **make up questions** they think will be on the vocabulary quiz.

Day 5: **Review vocabulary.**
Have students take the **Vocabulary Quiz.**

Teaching a Lesson

Word List (Days 1–5)

Each lesson begins with a word list of eight vocabulary words that contain the prefix or suffix that is the focus for the lesson. The part of speech and the definition are included for each word. Make two copies of the word list for each student. Have students keep one copy at school and take the second copy home so they can practice learning the words with their families. Follow the steps below to introduce each set of vocabulary words.

- Type each word in a large font. Print and mount the words on a 12" × 18" (30.5 cm × 46 cm) sheet of construction paper—four words to a sheet. Do the same for each definition. Cut apart the words and definitions to create individual cards. Display these enlarged word cards in a pocket chart for hands-on manipulation and practice throughout the week. At the end of each week, place the cards together on a ring and neatly store them in a hanging shoe organizer that has clear pockets. Students can play games with the cards independently or with partners. This will be a valuable resource during the review week in your teaching/lesson cycle.
- Write sentences on an overhead using the word list, and have students figure out the meaning of the word in the sentence based on the context. Ask students to write their definitions on a sentence strip and compare them to the exact definitions.

Vocabulary Sort (Day 2)

Following the list of prefixes or suffixes and their definitions is a list of the same eight words and definitions mixed up and arranged on cut-apart slips of paper. This activity is intended to provide hands-on practice with the words.

- Copy a class set of Vocabulary Sort cards on card stock, cut apart the words and definitions, place each set in a small envelope, and label it with the lesson's prefix or suffix. (You may want to laminate the cards for greater durability.) Have students independently match the words and definitions. Invite them to check their work by referring to their word lists.
- Give each student a large resealable plastic bag in which to store his or her Vocabulary Sort card envelopes after taking the quiz for that lesson. Encourage students to add sets of cards to this collection all year long. At least once every two weeks, give students time to match up all of the prefixes, suffixes, and definitions they have learned. This review will enhance students' vocabulary as they continue to use words they learned in previous lessons. Have students eliminate the words that they have mastered by placing them in a separate "Mastered" envelope in order to keep everything manageable. Watching the "Mastered" envelope fill up will build self-confidence and reinforce only the words that need focus.

Application and Practice (Day 3)

This activity page is intended to give students the opportunity to apply their vocabulary knowledge by working with the words and their definitions.

- Copy the Application and Practice page for each student. Have students independently match the vocabulary words to the correct definitions, or use the words to fill-in-the-blank. A word box is provided to allow students to keep track of the words used in the matching activity. Have students independently complete the crossword puzzle at the bottom. Correct the activities as a class to reinforce vocabulary and correct mistakes.

Read-Around Review (Day 3)

This set of cut-apart cards includes the word definitions for all eight words presented in a practical context. Many of the definitions have been reworded to encourage students to think and apply what they have learned about the meanings of the words. Have students use these cards to play an interactive game.

- Copy a set of cards on card stock for each small group of three to four students. Cut apart the cards and laminate them. Place each set of cards in an envelope, and write the title Read-Around Review at the top. Label the envelope with the corresponding prefix or suffix group (e.g., *pro-*).
- Give each group a set of cards. Ask students to divide the cards equally among the group. Have students silently read their cards several times. Discuss any questions students have before beginning the game. Tell the group that the student who has the clue card that says *I have the first card* will begin the game by reading aloud his or her card. After the first card is read aloud, have the student with the answer to the clue read aloud his or her card. Tell students to continue until they get back to the first card.

Games (Days 1 & 4)

Playing games is a fun way to reinforce learning. Use these games to introduce, extend, or review each lesson. Each week, build upon your students' mastery of prefixes and suffixes by adding challenging words from previous lessons.

- **Vocabulary Charades/Quick Draw**: Divide the class into two teams. Cut apart the words from the Vocabulary Sort and put them into a bowl. Invite four students from each team to pull a word out of the bowl. Give them a few minutes to get together with several students to come up with a way to act out the vocabulary word. Award points to the teams who correctly guess the word. Use this same activity as a Quick Draw game.
- **Mystery Word**: Cut apart words from the Vocabulary Sort and tape them to students' backs. Encourage them to not give away each other's word. Invite students to ask questions about the words taped on their backs and to give clues to their classmates. Challenge students to think of situations and contexts in which the words apply. Use this game after completing several lessons so students do not have duplicate words.
- **Word Hunt**: Divide the class into teams. Give students 15 minutes to search through any book to find prefixes or suffixes they have learned. Have them write down the words they find. Award points for words that the other groups did not find. Create a combined class list of new words and add to it for each lesson.

Assessment (Day 5)

- **Vocabulary Quiz**: Use the 15-question quiz at the end of each lesson to assess students' learning. The quizzes include fill-in-the-bubble and fill-in-the-blank questions to help prepare students for standardized tests. It is suggested that a word list be written on the board to assist students in recalling the words for that section.
- **Review Test**: A 15-question review test follows every two lessons. Each test assesses students' knowledge using fill-in-the-bubble and analogy formats. Before administering the test, review what an analogy is and how to answer this type of question.

Word List: e-, ex-

e-, ex-	out, out of, outside

Vocabulary	**Definitions**
eject (v)	to throw **out** with force, authority, or influence
emit (v)	to send **out** something like a sound or smell
erupt (v)	to force **out** or release something; to explode
exceed (v)	to go **out** beyond; to be **outside** and beyond what is expected
exclude (v)	to leave **out**
exhale (v)	to breathe **out**
expand (v)	to stretch **out**; to make or become larger
extinguish (v)	to put **out** a fire; to bring to an end

Vocabulary Sort: e-, ex-

Cut apart the words and definitions. Match each word to its definition. Check your answers by referring to the word list.

extinguish	**e**ject	**ex**hale	**ex**ceed
expand	**e**mit	**ex**clude	**e**rupt

to stretch **out**; to make or become larger	to put **out** a fire; to bring to an end
to leave **out**	to breathe **out**
to force **out** or release something; to explode	to throw **out** with force, authority, or influence
to send **out** something like a sound or smell	to go **out** beyond; to be **outside** and beyond what is expected

Application and Practice: e-, ex-

Matching Clues to Vocabulary ·

Write the word that matches each clue.
Use each word only once.

exceed	expand	exhale	erupt
exclude	eject	emit	extinguish

1 _____ I grabbed the hose to do this to the fire.

2 _____ My lungs help me do this all day long.

3 _____ The player's behavior was so appalling that we were surprised the referee did not do this to him.

4 _____ My mom was proud because she knew I would meet my goals or do better.

5 _____ People fled the village when they heard the volcano was about to do *this*.

6 _____ Some selective clubs are very picky about who can become a member, and they do not allow some people to join.

7 _____ I need to make my suitcase do this so I can fit all my clothes in it.

8 _____ This word describes a smell coming from a trashcan as you walk by.

Crossword Puzzle ·

Write the word that matches each clue to complete the puzzle.

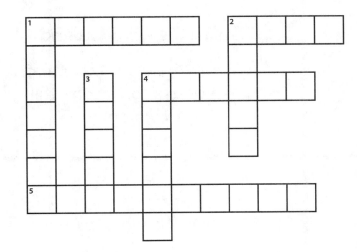

Across
1. action of the lungs as you breathe out
2. a sound or smell comes out
4. when you do better than you expected
5. to bring to an end

Down
1. to leave out
2. to throw out something with force
3. what an active volcano might do
4. to make something larger

More Prefixes and Suffixes © 2007 Creative Teaching Press

Read-Around Review: *e-, ex-*

I have the first card.

Who has the word that means to leave **out** of a group?

I have the prefixes **e-** and **ex-**.

Who has the word that means to throw something or someone **out**?

I have the word **exclude**.

Who has the word that means to send **out** a sound or smell such as an odor?

I have the word **eject**.

Who has the word that means to go **out** beyond what is expected?

I have the word **emit**.

Who has the word that means to breathe **out**?

I have the word **exceed**.

Who has the word that means to stretch **out**?

I have the word **exhale**.

Who has the word that means to put **out** a fire or to bring to an end?

I have the word **expand**.

Who has the word that means to explode or force something **out** violently?

I have the word **extinguish**.

Who has the prefix that means **out** or **outside of**?

I have the word **erupt**.

Who has the first card?

More Prefixes and Suffixes © 2007 Creative Teaching Press

Vocabulary Quiz: e-, ex-

Shade in the bubble for the correct word.

1 This is what you do if you leave a friend out of a game at recess.
    Ⓐ **exceed**   Ⓑ **expand**   Ⓒ **exclude**   Ⓓ **eject**

2 Your lungs help you do this, which is an essential part of life.
    Ⓐ **erupt**   Ⓑ **emit**   Ⓒ **exceed**   Ⓓ **exhale**

3 If a glowstick gives off a soft light, it does this.
    Ⓐ **emits**   Ⓑ **ejects**   Ⓒ **extinguishes**   Ⓓ **expand**

4 You can do this to some suitcases to be able to pack more clothes.
    Ⓐ **eject**   Ⓑ **emit**   Ⓒ **erupt**   Ⓓ **expand**

5 If a volcano does this, then people living nearby will have to evacuate.
    Ⓐ **extinguishes**   Ⓑ **erupts**   Ⓒ **ejects**   Ⓓ **expands**

6 If you enter a restricted area, the authorities will do *this* to you.
    Ⓐ **eject**   Ⓑ **erupt**   Ⓒ **emit**   Ⓓ **expert**

7 This is what you do to the campfire before going to bed.
    Ⓐ **erupt**   Ⓑ **exhale**   Ⓒ **expanded**   Ⓓ **extinguish**

8 This is what you hope to do to your own expectations in life.
    Ⓐ **expand**   Ⓑ **exceed**   Ⓒ **emit**   Ⓓ **eject**

Write the correct form of the word on the line so the sentence makes sense and is grammatically correct.

9 My dog _____ my expectations when he learned to sit in only a day!

10 In your report, please remember to _____ any slang words.

11 A flower can _____ a strange smell.

12 The hockey players were _____ from the game for fighting.

13 The scientist predicted that the volcano would begin to _____ within the hour.

14 I need you to _____ this paragraph of your story by including more details.

15 It is impossible to _____ all the air in your lungs to blow up the raft in one breath!

Word List: in-

in-	in, inside, into

Vocabulary	Definitions
include (v)	to be a part of; to be a member **in**
inflate (v)	to put air or gas **into** something; to fill **in** with air or gas
inhale (v)	to breathe **in**
inject (v)	to force **into** something; to force fluid **in**
inspect (v)	to look **in**; to look carefully at something
inspire (v)	to influence someone **in** a positive way or direction; to breathe life **into**
instruct (v)	to teach; to give knowledge **into** something
invite (v)	to ask someone **in**

Vocabulary Sort: in-

Cut apart the words and definitions. Match each word to its definition. Check your answers by referring to the word list.

inspire	**in**ject	**in**hale	**in**vite
inspect	**in**flate	**in**clude	**in**struct

to ask someone **in**	to teach; to give knowledge **into** something
to put air or gas **into** something; to fill **in** with air or gas	to look **in**; to look carefully at something
to influence someone **in** a positive way or direction; to breathe life **into**	to breathe **in**
to force **into** something; to force fluid **in**	to be a part of; to be a member **in**

Application and Practice: in-

Sentence Fill-ins

Complete each sentence with the correct word. Use each word only once.

inhale	include	inspire	invite
inspect	instruct	inflate	inject

1. Whom do you feel will _____ you to become a better person?

2. "I need you to _____ slowly for me," said Dr. Blumenthal.

3. We need to _____ the tires on my bike.

4. Did you remember to _____ pajamas on your list for the sleepover?

5. The veterinarian had to _____ Callie with some fluids to help her stay healthy.

6. The mechanic took three hours to _____ my car.

7. She helped _____ the young girl on how to tie her shoe.

8. Would you like to _____ your friend Tom to the party?

Crossword Puzzle

Write the word that matches each clue to complete the puzzle.

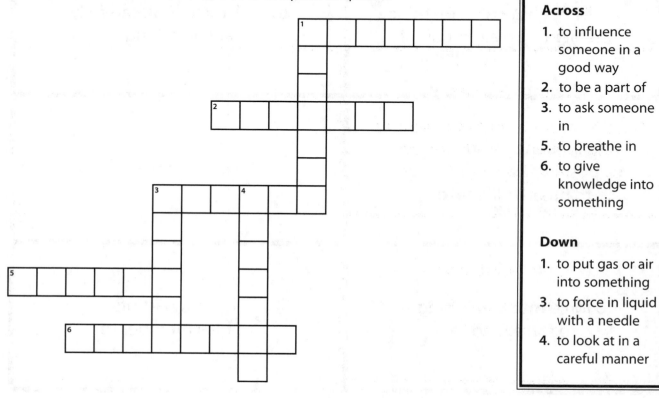

Across
1. to influence someone in a good way
2. to be a part of
3. to ask someone in
5. to breathe in
6. to give knowledge into something

Down
1. to put gas or air into something
3. to force in liquid with a needle
4. to look at in a careful manner

More Prefixes and Suffixes © 2007 Creative Teaching Press

Read-Around Review: in-

I have the first card.

Who has the word that describes what you do when you breathe **in** with your lungs?

I have the prefix **in-**.

Who has the word that describes what a nurse does when she puts fluids **into** your body through a needle when giving a shot?

I have the word **inhale**.

Who has the word that describes what you do when you put air **into** a soccer ball?

I have the word **inject**.

Who has the word that describes how a jeweler looks carefully at a ring?

I have the word **inflate**.

Who has the word that means you welcome someone **in** or ask them to join you?

I have the word **inspect**.

Who has the word that describes what you do when you teach something?

I have the word **invite**.

Who has the word that describes how a person is influenced **in** a good way?

I have the word **instruct**.

Who has the word that means to be a member **in**?

I have the word **inspire**.

Who has the prefix that means **in**, **inside**, or **into**?

I have the word **include**.

Who has the first card?

Vocabulary Quiz: in-

Shade in the bubble for the correct word.

1 You have just taught your dog how to sit. What did you do?
     Ⓐ **injected**   Ⓑ **instructed**   Ⓒ **inspected**   Ⓓ **inspired**

2 Shelly asked Jill to come to her birthday party. What did she do?
     Ⓐ **invited**   Ⓑ **inspired**   Ⓒ **inflated**   Ⓓ **inhaled**

3 The gardener forced fertilizer into the sprinkler system. What did he do?
     Ⓐ **inspected**   Ⓑ **inspired**   Ⓒ **inflated**   Ⓓ **injected**

4 Katie stopped to smell the flowers in the garden. What did she do?
     Ⓐ **inflated**   Ⓑ **instructed**   Ⓒ **inhaled**   Ⓓ **inspected**

5 The clown needed to do this to his balloons before he could create animals.
     Ⓐ **inflate**   Ⓑ **inhale**   Ⓒ **inspire**   Ⓓ **inject**

6 Dawn set an example for Linda by helping animals at the local shelter. Linda began doing the same thing. What did Dawn do to Linda?
     Ⓐ **inspected**   Ⓑ **instructed**   Ⓒ **inflated**   Ⓓ **inspired**

7 Before selling his home, Mitch had to hire someone to carefully look for termite damage. What did the person do to his home?
     Ⓐ **instructed**   Ⓑ **inflated**   Ⓒ **inspected**   Ⓓ **inflated**

8 Paul didn't want anyone to feel excluded from his pool party. He called everyone so that they were all what?
     Ⓐ **inflated**   Ⓑ **included**   Ⓒ **inspired**   Ⓓ **inspected**

Write the correct form of the word on the line so the sentence makes sense and is grammatically correct.

9 Did you have your car _____ by a mechanic before going on your trip?

10 My farewell party will _____ a piñata, ice cream sundaes, and prizes for games.

11 You _____ me to be kind to others when I see you do good deeds.

12 When you are ready, I will insert the needle to _____ the medicine.

13 Alexa will need to _____ deeply before diving under the water.

14 Mrs. Juarez finds it difficult to _____ a student who doesn't pay attention.

15 I will need to make sure to _____ the entire office over for the holiday dinner.

More Prefixes and Suffixes © 2007 Creative Teaching Press

Name _____   Date _____

Review Test: e-, ex-, and in-

Shade in the bubble for the correct word.

1 What do you call what someone does when they put an end to something?
     Ⓐ **inflate**   Ⓑ **extinguish**   Ⓒ **exclude**   Ⓓ **eject**

2 Did you remember to _____ the Table of Contents in the front of your report?
     Ⓐ **include**   Ⓑ **exclude**   Ⓒ **inject**   Ⓓ **inhale**

3 My brother is learning how to read because his tutor does this. What does his tutor do?
     Ⓐ **inspects**   Ⓑ **erupts**   Ⓒ **instructs**   Ⓓ **injects**

4 "Now blow a deep breath out," said Dr. Lung.
     Ⓐ **inhale**   Ⓑ **exclude**   Ⓒ **exceed**   Ⓓ **exhale**

5 The volcano is about to send lava out all over the mountain!
     Ⓐ **erupt**   Ⓑ **include**   Ⓒ **exceed**   Ⓓ **expand**

6 When you eat too much, you might feel your stomach get larger.
     Ⓐ **inhale**   Ⓑ **expand**   Ⓒ **exclude**   Ⓓ **inspire**

7 Kookaburra birds send out funny sounds when they are excited.
     Ⓐ **exhale**   Ⓑ **eject**   Ⓒ **exceed**   Ⓓ **emit**

8 Did you remember to _____ your backpack for your pencil before asking for another?
     Ⓐ **inflate**   Ⓑ **inject**   Ⓒ **inspect**   Ⓓ **instruct**

9 I'm going to ask Gina if she wants to come over and play with me.
     Ⓐ **invite**   Ⓑ **inflate**   Ⓒ **inspect**   Ⓓ **inject**

10 A person who leaves people out of a game is a person who will lose friends quickly.
     Ⓐ **include**   Ⓑ **exclude**   Ⓒ **expand**   Ⓓ **inspect**

11 It's not good when you spend more than you make. That's when you do what to your budget?
     Ⓐ **eject**   Ⓑ **extinguish**   Ⓒ **inject**   Ⓓ **exceed**

12 The manager had to _____ the obnoxious man from the restaurant.
     Ⓐ **exceed**   Ⓑ **emit**   Ⓒ **eject**   Ⓓ **expand**

13 Before going on a long trip, Tran did this to his tires.
     Ⓐ **ejected**   Ⓑ **injected**   Ⓒ **excluded**   Ⓓ **inflated**

14 Solve the analogy.
     inhale : breathe in :: _____ : breathe out

15 Solve the analogy.
     carry : drop :: _____ : deflate

Word List: non-

non-	not

Vocabulary	Definitions
nondairy (adj)	**not** made with milk or other dairy products
nonfat (adj)	does **not** contain fat
nonfiction (adj)	**not** fiction; real; true; factual
nonhuman (adj)	**not** of the human species
nonprofit (adj)	**not** in the business to make a profit; for charity
nonsense (n)	something that does **not** make sense; something that is silly or foolish
nontoxic (adj)	**not** harmful
nonverbal (adj)	**not** using speech; using little or no oral language

Vocabulary Sort: non-

Cut apart the words and definitions. Match each word to its definition. Check your answers by referring to the word list.

nonverbal	**non**sense	**non**dairy	**non**toxic
nonprofit	**non**fat	**non**human	**non**fiction

not fiction; real; true; factual	**not** in the business to make a profit; for charity
does **not** contain fat	**not** of the human species
not made with milk or other dairy products	**not** harmful
not using speech; using little or no oral language	something that does **not** make sense; something that is silly or foolish

Application and Practice: non-

Matching Clues to Vocabulary ·

Write the word that matches each clue.
Use each word only once.

nonhuman	nonfat	nonfiction	nontoxic
nonsense	nondairy	nonprofit	nonverbal

1 _____ I am allergic to milk, so all of my food products must fit into this category.

2 _____ All paints and chemicals that are safe around children should be labeled with this word.

3 _____ Ken's story was just too silly to ever believe, so I told him it was this.

4 _____ A charitable organization is one that helps people or animals without trying to earn money for selfish reasons.

5 _____ That book was completely based on his own life story. It would be classified as this.

6 _____ The tale is of a creature that is half horse and half man. The creature is specified as this.

7 _____ Many snacks with this label can still make people gain weight due to the flour and sugar.

8 _____ Although her dog could not speak, he could definitely communicate what he wanted by using this type of behavior.

Crossword Puzzle ·

Write the word that matches each clue to complete the puzzle.

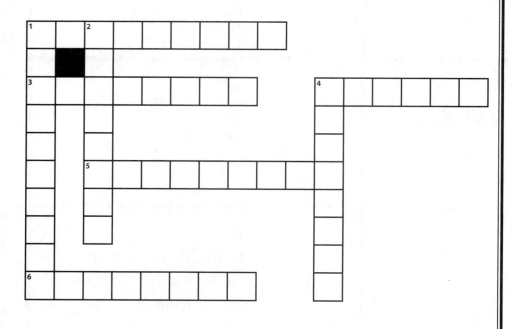

Across

1. not using oral language to communicate
3. not made with milk or other dairy products
4. does not contain fat
5. an organization that helps others without making a profit
6. not in the species of mammals called humans

Down

1. a true story based on facts
2. something that is silly or unbelievable
4. not harmful; safe

More Prefixes and Suffixes © 2007 Creative Teaching Press

Read-Around Review: non-

I have the first card.

Who has the word that is often printed on products telling you that it's **not** harmful?

I have the word **nondairy**.

Who has the word that describes books that are factual and true?

I have the word **nontoxic**.

Who has the word that describes anything that is **not** of the human species?

I have the word **nonfiction**.

Who has the word that describes a charity that earns money for purposes other than itself?

I have the word **nonhuman**.

Who has the word that describes something that is totally ridiculous or silly?

I have the word **nonprofit**.

Who has the prefix that means **not**?

I have the word **nonsense**.

Who has the word that describes a product that does **not** contain any fat?

I have the prefix **non-**.

Who has the word that describes a method of communication that does **not** include oral speech?

I have the word **nonfat**.

Who has the word that is written on products that do **not** use any dairy ingredients?

I have the word **nonverbal**.

Who has the first card?

More Prefixes and Suffixes © 2007 Creative Teaching Press

Name _____ Date _____

Vocabulary Quiz: non-

Shade in the bubble for the correct word.

1　What does Daniel look for on products to make sure he won't have an allergic reaction to milk?
　Ⓐ **nonsense**　　Ⓑ **nontoxic**　　Ⓒ **nonfat**　　Ⓓ **nondairy**

2　What might you hear someone say if he or she doesn't believe you?
　Ⓐ **nonhuman**　　Ⓑ **nonsense**　　Ⓒ **nonfiction**　　Ⓓ **nontoxic**

3　All cleaning products that do not say this can be harmful if swallowed.
　Ⓐ **nonprofit**　　Ⓑ **nonhuman**　　Ⓒ **nontoxic**　　Ⓓ **nonfat**

4　The scientist discovered some small animal bones. What kind of bones were they?
　Ⓐ **nonhuman**　　Ⓑ **nontoxic**　　Ⓒ **nondairy**　　Ⓓ **nonprofit**

5　Each year, thousands of families donate money to different organizations to help others. What kind of organizations are they?
　Ⓐ **nonfat**　　Ⓑ **nonhuman**　　Ⓒ **nonverbal**　　Ⓓ **nonprofit**

6　If you were on a diet, what kind of ice cream would you choose?
　Ⓐ **nondairy**　　Ⓑ **nontoxic**　　Ⓒ **nonfat**　　Ⓓ **nonprofit**

7　Kirsten enjoyed reading the books on the bestseller list that were factual and true. Which books did she read?
　Ⓐ **nonfiction**　　Ⓑ **nonfat**　　Ⓒ **nonsense**　　Ⓓ **nonhuman**

8　Apes have been taught to use sign language to communicate. What kind of communication is that?
　Ⓐ **nonfiction**　　Ⓑ **nonsense**　　Ⓒ **nontoxic**　　Ⓓ **nonverbal**

Write the correct form of the word on the line so the sentence makes sense and is grammatically correct.

9　The librarian couldn't believe how much the children loved the _____ books more than the fictional stories.

10　Alice enjoys making up _____ words that nobody else will understand.

11　The chocolate bars were supposed to be _____, but she couldn't understand how that was possible.

12　In any safe home, most cleaning supplies will be _____.

13　The _____ organization raised money for animals in an animal sanctuary.

14　Soy milk is a tasty alternative if you can only drink _____ products.

15　The toddler was still in the _____ stage, so he would often cry to get what he wanted.

More Prefixes and Suffixes © 2007 Creative Teaching Press

Word List: il-, im-, in-, ir-

il-, im-, in-, ir-   not

Vocabulary	Definitions
illegal (adj)	**not** within the law; **not** acceptable
immobile (adj)	**not** able to move; **not** movable; motionless
impaired (adj)	**not** of full quality, ability, or strength; damaged
impede (v)	to **not** be able to move forward; to block the passage
inactive (adj)	**not** in use; idle; **not** active
incapable (adj)	unable; **not** having the ability
irregular (adj)	**not** following a pattern; **not** regular
irreversible (adj)	**not** able to change back to a former state; impossible to revert back

SPEED LIMIT 35

More Prefixes and Suffixes © 2007 Creative Teaching Press

Vocabulary Sort: il-, im-, in-, ir-

Cut apart the words and definitions. Match each word to its definition. Check your answers by referring to the word list.

irreversible	**in**capable	**im**paired	**il**legal
irregular	**in**active	**im**mobile	**im**pede

not able to move; **not** movable; motionless	**not** in use; idle; **not** active
to **not** be able to move forward; to block the passage	**not** following a pattern; **not** regular
not able to change back to a former state; impossible to revert back	**not** within the law; **not** acceptable
unable; **not** having the ability	**not** of full quality, ability, or strength; damaged

More Prefixes and Suffixes © 2007 Creative Teaching Press

Name _____   Date _____

Application and Practice: il-, im-, in-, ir-

Sentence Fill-ins ·····························

Complete each sentence with the correct word. Use each word only once.

immobile	impede	inactive	irreversible
illegal	impaired	irregular	incapable

1. Did you know that it's _____ to ride in a car without a seatbelt in some states?

2. Her dress had an _____ pattern that was very colorful.

3. Even though he tried, he seemed _____ of keeping his room clean.

4. The doctor warned her that the surgery was _____, so she needed to be sure that she wanted it done.

5. The chipmunk was hibernating, so it was _____.

6. Brenton had ear surgery because a tumor resulted in _____ hearing.

7. Without tires, the car was certainly _____.

8. The orange cones in the road were placed there to _____ drivers from ruining the new cement.

Crossword Puzzle ·····························

Write the word that matches each clue to complete the puzzle.

Across

4. damaged to the point of not having full capacity to use something
6. impossible to change back
7. not moving or busy; still

Down

1. unable to do something
2. not regular
3. to block the path of something
4. unable to move
5. against the law

Read-Around Review: il-, im-, in-, ir-

I have the first card.

Who has the word that describes what you are doing if you are **not** able to move forward?

I have the word **illegal**.

Who has the word that means something that will **not** change back to its original form?

I have the word **impede**.

Who has the prefixes that mean **not**?

I have the word **irreversible**.

Who has the word that describes a person who has both legs in casts and can**not** move?

I have the prefixes **il-**, **im-**, **in-**, and **ir-**.

Who has the word that means to **not** follow a pattern?

I have the word **immobile**.

Who has the word that describes **not** being able to do something such as a back flip?

I have the word **irregular**.

Who has the word that describes how you are if you are sitting still and **not** active?

I have the word **incapable**.

Who has the word that describes a person who has partially lost the use of one of his or her senses and does **not** have full ability?

I have the word **inactive**.

Who has the word that describes the type of act that police officers try to prevent because it is **not** acceptable?

I have the word **impaired**.

Who has the first card?

More Prefixes and Suffixes © 2007 Creative Teaching Press

Vocabulary Quiz: il-, im-, in-, ir-

Shade in the bubble for the correct word.

1. Which word describes a person who wants to do something but doesn't have the ability?
   - Ⓐ **irregular**
   - Ⓑ **inactive**
   - Ⓒ **irreversible**
   - Ⓓ **incapable**

2. Isis had to think about cutting her hair short, since the decision would be what?
   - Ⓐ **impede**
   - Ⓑ **illegal**
   - Ⓒ **immobile**
   - Ⓓ **irreversible**

3. Which word describes an act that breaks the law of a city, county, or state?
   - Ⓐ **illegal**
   - Ⓑ **irregular**
   - Ⓒ **irreversible**
   - Ⓓ **incapable**

4. While Marcus is napping, his body is this even though his brain is functioning.
   - Ⓐ **irregular**
   - Ⓑ **inactive**
   - Ⓒ **incapable**
   - Ⓓ **impaired**

5. After Robert's injury to his hand, his finger usage was not what it used to be. What was it?
   - Ⓐ **impaired**
   - Ⓑ **irregular**
   - Ⓒ **impede**
   - Ⓓ **illegal**

6. Caisha noticed that the birds weren't flying in their normal formation. What was it?
   - Ⓐ **illegal**
   - Ⓑ **irreversible**
   - Ⓒ **incapable**
   - Ⓓ **irregular**

7. The car was parked for too long and not driven. Now it can't be moved because the battery is dead. What is it?
   - Ⓐ **immobile**
   - Ⓑ **impaired**
   - Ⓒ **illegal**
   - Ⓓ **incapable**

8. Noise disturbed the author, so she worked in a silent room. Any noise might do what to her train of thought?
   - Ⓐ **inactivate**
   - Ⓑ **immobile**
   - Ⓒ **impede**
   - Ⓓ **incapable**

Write the correct form of the word on the line so the sentence makes sense and is grammatically correct.

9. Ashley loved animals so much that she was _____ of understanding how others might not.

10. Odd shapes were scattered across the canvas in an _____ pattern, making the abstract painting seem unbalanced and strange.

11. The taxi was _____, since the traffic had the freeway at a complete stop.

12. Taking care of your skin is important, since the damage can be _____.

13. Tom loved working out in the gym, while Keith loved being _____.

14. It is _____ to drive over the speed limit.

15. The mudslide _____ the drivers from being able to return home after the storm.

Review Test: non- and il-, im-, in-, ir-

Shade in the bubble for the correct word.

1 What do you call a liquid that is not harmful?
Ⓐ **inactive**　　　Ⓑ **immobile**　　　Ⓒ **nonsense**　　　Ⓓ **nontoxic**

2 If something is blocking your way, what is it doing to you?
Ⓐ **impeding**　　　Ⓑ **inactive**　　　Ⓒ **nonprofit**　　　Ⓓ **illegal**

3 Even though Molly took piano lessons for three years, she still can't play a whole song. What is she?
Ⓐ **immobile**　　　Ⓑ **incapable**　　　Ⓒ **irregular**　　　Ⓓ **nonhuman**

4 Lupe had eye surgery, but she still can't see at night. What is her vision?
Ⓐ **inactive**　　　Ⓑ **nonverbal**　　　Ⓒ **impaired**　　　Ⓓ **nonprofit**

5 Lance enjoys reading the type of books that are factual and teach him new information. What kind of books are they?
Ⓐ **nonfiction**　　　Ⓑ **nonhuman**　　　Ⓒ **nonprofit**　　　Ⓓ **nonsense**

6 After the fall, Cindy had to lie in bed with her leg raised in a cast for three weeks. She was what?
Ⓐ **nonsense**　　　Ⓑ **immobile**　　　Ⓒ **irregular**　　　Ⓓ **irreversible**

7 What type of word is *frilipazoid*?
Ⓐ **impaired**　　　Ⓑ **nonsense**　　　Ⓒ **nonverbal**　　　Ⓓ **inactive**

8 An organization that raises money for worthy causes might be described as what?
Ⓐ **nonprofit**　　　Ⓑ **nonfat**　　　Ⓒ **nonhuman**　　　Ⓓ **nonsense**

9 A person who does one of these actions will find him- or herself arrested.
Ⓐ **illegal**　　　Ⓑ **immobile**　　　Ⓒ **impaired**　　　Ⓓ **irregular**

10 Which word describes something that cannot be returned to its original form or ability?
Ⓐ **impeded**　　　Ⓑ **immobile**　　　Ⓒ **irreversible**　　　Ⓓ **nontoxic**

11 Kyle bought a shirt at a store that didn't have a normal pattern. This type of pattern is called what?
Ⓐ **inactive**　　　Ⓑ **nonhuman**　　　Ⓒ **nonfat**　　　Ⓓ **irregular**

12 Which word describes a person who sits around watching television all day?
Ⓐ **nonhuman**　　　Ⓑ **inactive**　　　Ⓒ **illegal**　　　Ⓓ **impeded**

13 Apes, lemurs, and ferrets fit into which category?
Ⓐ **nonfat**　　　Ⓑ **nonhuman**　　　Ⓒ **nontoxic**　　　Ⓓ **nonsense**

14 Solve the analogy.
calm : excited :: _____ : active

15 Solve the analogy.
nonfat : no fat :: _____ : no milk or dairy products

More Prefixes and Suffixes © 2007 Creative Teaching Press

Word List: pro-

pro-	for, in favor of, forward, positive

Vocabulary	Definitions
probable (adj)	likely; likely to move in a **positive** direction
proceed (v)	to move **forward**; to go; to follow through with an idea or plan
projectile (n)	a **forward**-moving object that was thrown or self-powered
prolong (v)	to draw out; to make something moving **forward** last longer
promotion (n)	a movement **forward** in a company; a movement up into a better position in a job
propel (v)	to cause to move **forward**
prospect (n)	the act of looking **forward** in anticipation of something to come
protest (v)	to **forward** a complaint, objection, or display of unwillingness

Vocabulary Sort: pro-

Cut apart the words and definitions. Match each word to its definition. Check your answers by referring to the word list.

prolong	**pro**motion	**pro**spect	**pro**jectile
propel	**pro**bable	**pro**test	**pro**ceed

to **forward** a complaint, objection, or display of unwillingness	to cause to move **forward**
to move **forward**; to go; to follow through with an idea or plan	a movement **forward** in a company; a movement up into a better position in a job
to draw out; to make something moving **forward** last longer	the act of looking **forward** in anticipation of something to come
likely; likely to move in a **positive** direction	a **forward**-moving object that was thrown or self-powered

More Prefixes and Suffixes © 2007 Creative Teaching Press

Application and Practice: pro-

Sentence Fill-ins

Complete each sentence with the correct
word. Use each word only once.

prospect	prolong	proceed	projectile
propel	promotion	probable	protest

1　She will _____ the testing of products on animals by not buying those items.

2　The paper airplane is a type of _____ that can fly through the sky.

3　The construction plans were approved. Now the workers can _____ with building the new house.

4　He was enjoying the vacation so much that he wished he could _____ it another week.

5　Arturo's hard work earned him a _____ in the company with a pay raise and better benefits.

6　It was _____ that Raja would roll a number of two or larger in a dice game.

7　He had a good _____ for college if he kept playing basketball in high school.

8　The rocket launcher could _____ the rocket at a faster speed than ever imagined.

Crossword Puzzle

Write the word that matches each clue to complete the puzzle.

Across

2. to complain or object
3. to move ahead with a plan
5. to look forward in anticipation
6. to move something forward

Down

1. an object thrown forward with great speed
2. likely
3. to move forward in a company; a better job
4. to make something last longer

Read-Around Review: pro-

I have the first card.

Who has the word that describes the **favorable** chance of something happening?

I have the word **proceed**.

Who has the word that describes an objection to an idea or action?

I have the word **probable**.

Who has the word that names an object thrown **forward** with force?

I have the word **protest**.

Who has the word that describes the act of being excited about something that could happen?

I have the word **projectile**.

Who has the word that describes what people try to do when they want a weekend to last longer?

I have the word **prospect**.

Who has the word that describes what a ride at an amusement park might do when it moves you **forward** through water?

I have the word **prolong**.

Who has the word that describes what people get when their boss changes their job in a **positive** way?

I have the word **propel**.

Who has the prefix that means **for, in favor of, forward,** or **positive**?

I have the word **promotion**.

Who has the word that describes when a person is given permission to move **forward** with something?

I have the prefix **pro-**.

Who has the first card?

More Prefixes and Suffixes © 2007 Creative Teaching Press

Name _____   Date _____

Vocabulary Quiz: pro-

Shade in the bubble for the correct word.

1 After the train departed, the people were allowed to do this across the street.
Ⓐ **protest**   Ⓑ **prospect**   Ⓒ **propel**   Ⓓ **proceed**

2 She will do this if something goes against her beliefs.
Ⓐ **promotion**   Ⓑ **prolong**   Ⓒ **protest**   Ⓓ **prospect**

3 While walking down the street, the poor lady was hit with something thrown from a car. What could the object be called?
Ⓐ **projectile**   Ⓑ **prospect**   Ⓒ **promotion**   Ⓓ **prolonged**

4 His new position included a raise and a larger office. What did he get?
Ⓐ **probable**   Ⓑ **prospect**   Ⓒ **propel**   Ⓓ **promotion**

5 Sometimes people wish they could do this to the warm summer days.
Ⓐ **prolong**   Ⓑ **prospect**   Ⓒ **propel**   Ⓓ **proceed**

6 Mom and Dad had the chance for a quiet weekend because everyone would be out of the house. What is this kind of chance called?
Ⓐ **prospect**   Ⓑ **proceed**   Ⓒ **prolong**   Ⓓ **propel**

7 The force could move them quickly through the water slide. What do we call this type of movement?
Ⓐ **proceed**   Ⓑ **propel**   Ⓒ **probable**   Ⓓ **promotion**

8 The weather forecaster stated that it was likely to rain tomorrow. How can we describe the chance for rain?
Ⓐ **probable**   Ⓑ **prolonged**   Ⓒ **protest**   Ⓓ **prospect**

Write the correct form of the word on the line so the sentence makes sense and is grammatically correct.

9 They went out to dinner to celebrate their mother's new _____ at work.

10 Before throwing any _____ into the air, make sure that the area is clear of people.

11 The company's employees will _____ if each worker is not given their yearly bonus.

12 It was _____ that she would get an A on her test, since she studied every night for a week.

13 Let's _____ with our plans to invent a robot that makes our bed.

14 Mr. Garcia enjoyed the _____ of getting his favorite author's autograph.

15 Elena tried to _____ the interview by asking more questions.

Word List: retro-, an-, anti-

| retro- | backward, back |
| an-, anti- | against, opposite |

Vocabulary	Definitions
antacid (n)	a substance that works **against** stomach acid
antibacterial (adj)	designed to fight **against** or kill bacteria
antidote (n)	a remedy or cure; something that works **against** a poison
antihistamine (n)	a medicine that works **against** colds and allergies
antonym (n)	a word that means the **opposite** of another word
retroactive (adj)	goes **back** to a prior time
retrofit (v)	to go **back** and install something that was not available at the time of original manufacturing
retrospective (adj)	characterized by looking **back** at the past and reflecting; related to the past

Vocabulary Sort: retro-, an-, anti-

Cut apart the words and definitions. Match each word to its definition. Check your answers by referring to the word list.

antidote	**an**tonym	**retro**active	**an**tacid
retrospective	**anti**bacterial	**retro**fit	**anti**histamine
a word that means the **opposite** of another word		characterized by looking **back** at the past and reflecting; related to the past	
to go **back** and install something that was not available at the time of original manufacturing		a substance that works **against** stomach acid	
a remedy or cure; something that works **against** a poison		designed to fight **against** or kill bacteria	
a medicine that works **against** colds and allergies		goes **back** to a prior time	

Application and Practice: retro-, an-, anti-

Sentence Fill-ins

Complete each sentence with the correct
word. Use each word only once.

antonym	retrospective	antihistamine	retrofit
antidote	antibacterial	retroactive	antacid

1 Jill took an _____ tablet to make her stomach feel better.

2 An _____ for *clean* is *messy*.

3 Shanelle's pay raise was _____ to six months ago.

4 Leroy's mom gave him an _____ for his allergies.

5 Dr. Pita is working on a new _____ for rattlesnake bites.

6 Brad bought some _____ soap for the kitchen of his new condo.

7 The movie was a _____ view of the past and the life of a pioneer child.

8 Robert was hired to _____ the old army tanks with new safety equipment.

Crossword Puzzle

Write the word that matches each clue to complete the puzzle.

Across

1. kind of soap that kills germs
3. related to looking back at the past
4. something you take to help an upset stomach
5. goes back to a previous time
6. opposite of another word

Down

2. a medicine to fight against colds and allergies
3. to install something new into a machine that already exists
4. a cure or remedy

More Prefixes and Suffixes © 2007 Creative Teaching Press

Read-Around Review: retro-, an-, anti-

I have the first card.

Who has the prefixes that mean **against** or **opposite**?

I have the word **antibacterial**.

Who has the word that means a cure for something that could otherwise be deadly?

I have the prefixes **an-** and **anti-**.

Who has the word that names a word with **opposite** meaning?

I have the word **antidote**.

Who has the word that names the substance adults might take when they have a stomachache?

I have the word **antonym**.

Who has the word that means to go **back** and install something new into a product that already exists?

I have the word **antacid**.

Who has the name of the medicine that works **against** a cold or allergy?

I have the word **retrofit**.

Who has the word that describes a person who is thinking and looking **back** on the past?

I have the word **antihistamine**.

Who has the word that describes something that goes **back** to a prior time?

I have the word **retrospective**.

Who has the word that describes a substance often added to soap products to kill bacterial germs?

I have the word **retroactive**.

Who has the first card?

Name _____ Date _____

Vocabulary Quiz: retro-, an-, anti-

Shade in the bubble for the correct word.

1 Meg bought a type of gel to kill germs, so she could wash her hands before eating her lunch. What kind of gel was it?

Ⓐ **antonym**   Ⓑ **antidote**   Ⓒ **antacid**   Ⓓ **antibacterial**

2 Many doctors around the world are working on these to help people survive diseases.

Ⓐ **antidotes**   Ⓑ **antihistamines**   Ⓒ **antacids**   Ⓓ **antonyms**

3 Some drivers like to customize their cars and trucks by hiring people to add special devices that were not originally installed. What do those people do?

Ⓐ **retroactive**   Ⓑ **retrofit**   Ⓒ **retrospect**   Ⓓ **antidote**

4 Dominic was thrilled to hear that his pay raise went back to the beginning of the year. What was his raise?

Ⓐ **retroactive**   Ⓑ **antidote**   Ⓒ **retrofitted**   Ⓓ **retrospective**

5 You can use a thesaurus to help find these kinds of words.

Ⓐ **antacids**   Ⓑ **retrofits**   Ⓒ **antonyms**   Ⓓ **antihistamines**

6 Many of these tablets fizz in water just like they do when a person takes them for a stomachache.

Ⓐ **antacids**   Ⓑ **antihistamines**   Ⓒ **antidotes**   Ⓓ **antibacterial**

7 The book was a reflection of life in the 1930s. What was the book?

Ⓐ **retroactive**   Ⓑ **full of antonyms**   Ⓒ **retrofitted**   Ⓓ **retrospective**

8 The doctor prescribed one of these medicines to help Jorge get over his cold a bit faster.

Ⓐ **antacid**   Ⓑ **antidote**   Ⓒ **retroactive**   Ⓓ **antihistamine**

Write the correct form of the word on the line so the sentence makes sense and is grammatically correct.

9 Her health insurance was _____ to the day she started working for the company three months ago.

10 There were so many choices of _____ to take for her cold, that Lucy found it difficult to choose one.

11 There is a different _____ for each type of deadly spider bite.

12 The _____ lotion smelled like vanilla and killed the germs on her hands.

13 Mr. Gonzalez took an _____ when he felt sick after eating too much food at dinner.

14 Can you name two _____ for the word *difficult*?

15 Dave wants to _____ his motorcycle with special gears and handlebars.

More Prefixes and Suffixes © 2007 Creative Teaching Press

Name _____ Date _____

Review Test: pro- and retro-, an-, anti-

Shade in the bubble for the correct word.

1 The _____ of playing football for a professional league team keeps Jerry motivated
   to practice every day.
   Ⓐ **antidote**   Ⓑ **prospect**   Ⓒ **projectile**   Ⓓ **retrospective**

2 The new roller coaster will _____ you through a tunnel at 60 miles per hour!
   Ⓐ **retrofit**   Ⓑ **projectile**   Ⓒ **prospect**   Ⓓ **propel**

3 The 50-year-old school was planning to _____ the buildings with new wiring.
   Ⓐ **proceed**   Ⓑ **prolong**   Ⓒ **retroactive**   Ⓓ **retrofit**

4 Try not to _____ getting ready in the morning or you'll be late for school.
   Ⓐ **promotion**   Ⓑ **prospect**   Ⓒ **prolong**   Ⓓ **proceed**

5 The game involved listing as many _____ for words as possible in 30 seconds.
   Ⓐ **antonyms**   Ⓑ **projectiles**   Ⓒ **antidotes**   Ⓓ **antacids**

6 Drivers must stop on the side of the road when they see or hear a siren. They may _____
   along their path once it has driven past.
   Ⓐ **proceed**   Ⓑ **prospect**   Ⓒ **protest**   Ⓓ **promotion**

7 Dr. Olson is working on the _____ to the bite from the brown recluse spider.
   Ⓐ **antidote**   Ⓑ **projectile**   Ⓒ **antacid**   Ⓓ **prospect**

8 When you have a cold, you probably take some medicine that includes _____.
   Ⓐ **antidotes**   Ⓑ **antihistamines**   Ⓒ **projectiles**   Ⓓ **antacids**

9 A boomerang is a _____ that is thrown and comes back to you.
   Ⓐ **prospect**   Ⓑ **prospect**   Ⓒ **promotion**   Ⓓ **projectile**

10 The story of the _____ movie took place in the late 1800s.
    Ⓐ **retroactive**   Ⓑ **protested**   Ⓒ **retrospective**   Ⓓ **promotion**

11 Her tax bill was _____ back to the time she first started making money without claiming it.
    Ⓐ **prospected**   Ⓑ **retroactive**   Ⓒ **promoted**   Ⓓ **probable**

12 The label on the _____ tablets says they are good for treating acid indigestion.
    Ⓐ **projectile**   Ⓑ **antidote**   Ⓒ **antacid**   Ⓓ **promotion**

13 It is highly _____ that the school's valedictorian will get accepted into a top college.
    Ⓐ **proceeding**   Ⓑ **antihistamine**   Ⓒ **retrofitting**   Ⓓ **probable**

14 The people climbed the century-old tree to _____ its removal.
    Ⓐ **promotion**   Ⓑ **protest**   Ⓒ **retrospective**   Ⓓ **antidote**

15 Leslie was given a _____ because of her dedication to the company.
    Ⓐ **projectile**   Ⓑ **protest**   Ⓒ **promotion**   Ⓓ **projectile**

Word List: ab-

ab-	away from

Vocabulary	Definitions
abduct (v)	to take someone **away** by force
abrupt (adj)	a sudden break **away from** something; unexpected change
absent (adj)	**away from** a location; not present; gone
absolve (v)	to set free **away from** guilt or obligation
absorb (v)	to take moisture **away from** an area by soaking up
abstain (v)	to refrain from; to stay **away from** participating
abstract (adj)	**away from** common thinking; not obvious
absurd (adj)	ridiculous; unbelievable; **away from** reality

Vocabulary Sort: ab-

Cut apart the words and definitions. Match each word to its definition. Check your answers by referring to the word list.

abrupt	**ab**sent	**ab**duct	**ab**solve
absurd	**ab**stain	**ab**stract	**ab**sorb

to take moisture **away from** an area by soaking up	to set free **away from** guilt or obligation
away from common thinking; not obvious	**away from** a location; not present; gone
to take someone **away** by force	ridiculous; unbelievable; **away from** reality
to refrain from; to stay **away from** participating	a sudden break **away from** something; unexpected change

Application and Practice: ab-

Sentence Fill-ins ·······································

Complete each sentence with the correct
word. Use each word only once.

absurd	abstain	absorb	abduct
abstract	absent	abrupt	absolve

1. Dad had to _____ me from blame when he saw the dog eating his pie.

2. Everyone thought it was an _____ idea, but he knew she could create a floor-scrubbing robot.

3. Evan had to _____ from drinking soda when he started wearing braces.

4. There were three students at home sick today. They were _____ from school.

5. John used a towel to _____ the spilled water from the carpet.

6. Mary made an _____ turn with the car, and I had to grab the handle to keep from falling over.

7. The images in the painting were _____ and hard to understand upon first viewing.

8. The man will be arrested by the police if he tries to _____ a child from the park.

Crossword Puzzle ·······································

Write the word that matches each clue to complete the puzzle.

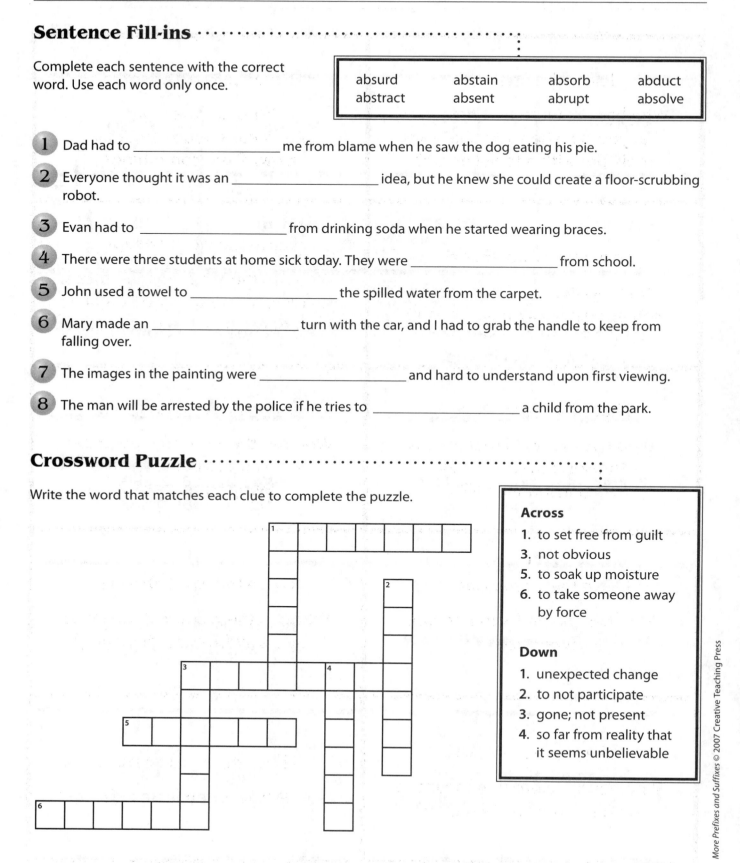

Across
1. to set free from guilt
3. not obvious
5. to soak up moisture
6. to take someone away by force

Down
1. unexpected change
2. to not participate
3. gone; not present
4. so far from reality that it seems unbelievable

Read-Around Review: ab-

I have the first card.

Who has the word that describes what you do when you take **away** moisture with a towel or rag?

I have the word **absolve**.

Who has the word that means a sudden break **away from** something?

I have the word **absorb**.

Who has the word that means someone is **away from** school?

I have the word **abrupt**.

Who has the word that describes an idea, painting, or book that is hard to understand at first?

I have the word **absent**.

Who has the word that means to take someone **away** against their will?

I have the word **abstract**.

Who has the word that describes a ridiculous plan, which is **away from** reality?

I have the word **abduct**.

Who has the prefix that means **away from**?

I have the word **absurd**.

Who has the word that means to stay **away from** participating?

I have the prefix **ab-**.

Who has the word that means to set free from an obligation?

I have the word **abstain**.

Who has the first card?

Vocabulary Quiz: ab-

Shade in the bubble for the correct word.

1 Brandy set her friend free from his obligation to help her move. What did she do?
    Ⓐ **abducted**   Ⓑ **absolved**   Ⓒ **abstained**   Ⓓ **absorbed**

2 The judge would not let the witness do this in the courtroom. He was ordered to answer all questions and fully participate.
    Ⓐ **abstract**   Ⓑ **absorb**   Ⓒ **abduct**   Ⓓ **abstain**

3 It took three visits to the museum for Harold to figure out what the pencil images formed on the artwork. What type of art was it?
    Ⓐ **abstract**   Ⓑ **abrupt**   Ⓒ **absolved**   Ⓓ **absurd**

4 Stacey's parents thought her story was a bit far-fetched, but she insisted it was true. Which word would they choose to describe her story?
    Ⓐ **absolved**   Ⓑ **abstain**   Ⓒ **absorb**   Ⓓ **absurd**

5 The car made this type of turn which caused Leslie to hit it.
    Ⓐ **abstain**   Ⓑ **abrupt**   Ⓒ **absolve**   Ⓓ **abduct**

6 The mother kept her child close so that no one would try to do this to him.
    Ⓐ **abduct**   Ⓑ **abstain**   Ⓒ **absolve**   Ⓓ **abstain**

7 Danielle helped her brother do this to the spilled milk with the paper towel.
    Ⓐ **absurd**   Ⓑ **abstract**   Ⓒ **absorb**   Ⓓ **abrupt**

8 The president was not at the meeting. What was he?
    Ⓐ **absent**   Ⓑ **absolved**   Ⓒ **abstract**   Ⓓ **abrupt**

Write the correct form of the word on the line so the sentence makes sense and is grammatically correct.

9 Tyler describes himself as an _____ artist because nothing is obvious. Only he truly sees what he paints.

10 We cannot make any _____ changes in routine without notifying everyone first.

11 I'm trying to _____ the juice with the dishrag before it stains the floor.

12 Jerrod tried to _____ his son from feeling guilty over the broken vase.

13 I will _____ from smoking because it's harmful to my health.

14 What an _____ idea! People will never fly with their arms like birds!

15 I'm sorry that I was _____ yesterday from the meeting. I was sick.

More Prefixes and Suffixes © 2007 Creative Teaching Press

Word List: ad-

| ad- | toward, to |

Vocabulary	Definitions
adapt (v)	to change for a new purpose; to move **toward** survival by changing
adhere (v)	to stick; to connect one thing to another; to move **toward** following rules or plans
adhesive (adj)	easily attached **to** something else; sticky
adjacent (adj)	near; **toward** something else; next **to**
admission (n)	right **to** enter; access
advance (v)	to move **toward** something
address (v)	to send **toward**; to direct the efforts or attention **to** something
adjourn (v)	to move an event or session **to** another place and time

Vocabulary Sort: ad-

Cut apart the words and definitions. Match each word to its definition. Check your answers by referring to the word list.

adjourn	**ad**vance	**ad**jacent	**ad**here
address	**ad**mission	**ad**hesive	**ad**apt

to stick; to connect one thing **to** another; to move **toward** following rules or plans	to move an event or session **to** another place and time
right **to** enter; access	to change for a new purpose; to move **toward** survival by changing
easily attached **to** something else; sticky	to move **toward** something
to send **toward**; to direct the efforts or attention **to** something	near; **toward** something else; next **to**

More Prefixes and Suffixes © 2007 Creative Teaching Press

Name _____ Date _____

Application and Practice: ad-

Sentence Fill-ins

Complete each sentence with the correct word. Use each word only once.

advance	adhere	admission	adapt
adjourn	adjacent	adhesive	address

1. Animals learn to _____ to habitat and climate changes in order to survive.

2. I will _____ to my original plan of buying a dark-colored couch for the main room.

3. These notepads have an _____ backing, so I can stick them anywhere and then remove them.

4. The shoe store is _____ to the clothing store, so I can quickly buy an entire outfit.

5. The museum was charging a $35.00 _____ fee to see the King Tut exhibit.

6. Gabriel asked me to _____ the invitation to his sister.

7. The motorcycle made a rapid _____ toward the finish line to win the race.

8. The committee had to _____ the meeting until the next day.

Crossword Puzzle

Write the word that matches each clue to complete the puzzle.

Across

1. to change in order to survive
4. sticky
5. to send to
6. to connect or stick to something
7. to move an event to another place and time

Down

1. right to enter
2. near; close to
3. to move toward something

Read-Around Review: ad-

I have the first card.

Who has the word that means to direct someone's attention **to** something?

I have the prefix **ad-**.

Who has the word that describes something that is sticky?

I have the word **address**.

Who has the word that means you have the right **to** enter or that you can come in?

I have the word **adhesive**.

Who has the word that means to move a session **to** another day?

I have the word **admission**.

Who has the word that means **to** move forward, such as in a chess game?

I have the word **adjourn**.

Who has the word that means to make necessary changes?

I have the word **advance**.

Who has the word that describes two objects next **to** each other?

I have the word **adapt**.

Who has the word that means to stick or connect **to** something?

I have the word **adjacent**.

Who has the prefix that means **toward** or **to**?

I have the word **adhere**.

Who has the first card?

Name _____   Date _____

Vocabulary Quiz: ad-

Shade in the bubble for the correct word.

1. When Jada showed the attendant the tickets for the movie, he gave her _____ to the theatre.
   Ⓐ **adhesive**   Ⓑ **admission**   Ⓒ **adaptation**   Ⓓ **advance**

2. Min thought it was funny that GoodFit Gym was right next door to The Polar Ice Cream Shop. The two shops were _____ to one another.
   Ⓐ **advance**   Ⓑ **adhere**   Ⓒ **adapt**   Ⓓ **adjacent**

3. Tucker was nervous because he would have to _____ an audience during his speech.
   Ⓐ **advance**   Ⓑ **address**   Ⓒ **adapt**   Ⓓ **adjourn**

4. The judge decided to _____ the trial until after lunch.
   Ⓐ **adapt**   Ⓑ **address**   Ⓒ **adjourn**   Ⓓ **advance**

5. In order to build the desk properly, you must put some glue in those holes. What is the glue?
   Ⓐ **adjourn**   Ⓑ **advice**   Ⓒ **adhesive**   Ⓓ **admission**

6. All creatures must learn to move or change when disaster strikes or they will die. They must _____ to their new environment.
   Ⓐ **advance**   Ⓑ **adapt**   Ⓒ **address**   Ⓓ **advance**

7. Maria wanted to follow the rules and plans exactly as they were stated. What did she do to the rules?
   Ⓐ **addressed**   Ⓑ **adapted**   Ⓒ **advanced**   Ⓓ **adhered**

8. There is a board game that has cards labeled "Proceed to GO" and "Collect $200." What else might the player do?
   Ⓐ **advance**   Ⓑ **admission**   Ⓒ **adjourn**   Ⓓ **adapt**

Write the correct form of the word on the line so the sentence makes sense and is grammatically correct.

9. Alison had to learn the new rules if she wanted to _____ to the next round in the game.

10. I'm going to _____ my complaint to the highest authority in the company.

11. We will have to _____ the photo shoot until tomorrow because the model cannot be here.

12. My school is _____ to a city park, so I get to play with my friends on my way home.

13. Leslie used an _____ to get the picture to stick to the paper.

14. Sam brought the coupon that would grant him free _____ to the roller rink.

15. Dezi wanted to _____ to her original math solution. She wasn't going to change her mind.

Name _____   Date _____

Review Test: ab- and ad-

Shade in the bubble for the correct word.

1 Julie wanted to _____ her gratitude to the hostess of the party.
   Ⓐ **advance**   Ⓑ **address**   Ⓒ **abstract**   Ⓓ **admission**

2 Micaela made an _____ motion with her hand that scared the dog.
   Ⓐ **abroad**   Ⓑ **abrupt**   Ⓒ **adhesive**   Ⓓ **adapt**

3 Years ago, many people thought the idea of an Internet connecting people around the world was _____.
   Ⓐ **absurd**   Ⓑ **absolved**   Ⓒ **abstained**   Ⓓ **adjacent**

4 The _____ was wearing off, so the poster was falling off the wall.
   Ⓐ **adjacent**   Ⓑ **admission**   Ⓒ **abstract**   Ⓓ **adhesive**

5 The price of _____ to a professional baseball game will be going up next year.
   Ⓐ **advancing**   Ⓑ **adaptation**   Ⓒ **admission**   Ⓓ **abstaining**

6 Lily had to _____ her brother from guilt over the car accident because it wasn't his fault.
   Ⓐ **absolve**   Ⓑ **abduct**   Ⓒ **adapt**   Ⓓ **abstain**

7 The club had to _____ its meeting for a month because the president was ill.
   Ⓐ **adjourn**   Ⓑ **adhesive**   Ⓒ **abstract**   Ⓓ **address**

8 Mrs. Franks was _____ for the beginning of the year so she could care for her new baby.
   Ⓐ **adhesive**   Ⓑ **abstaining**   Ⓒ **absolved**   Ⓓ **absent**

9 Hailey was able to _____ to the next level in her yoga class.
   Ⓐ **advance**   Ⓑ **abstain**   Ⓒ **abstract**   Ⓓ **adhere**

10 Mr. Guzman is hoping that the towel will _____ all of the liquid from the floor.
   Ⓐ **address**   Ⓑ **absolve**   Ⓒ **adjacent**   Ⓓ **absorb**

11 The athlete tried to _____ from all unhealthy foods and habits while training for the race.
   Ⓐ **abstain**   Ⓑ **adhere**   Ⓒ **adapt**   Ⓓ **advance**

12 The teacher decided to _____ to her original plan of not giving homework over the weekends.
   Ⓐ **adhere**   Ⓑ **abduct**   Ⓒ **abstain**   Ⓓ **absolve**

13 The bears in the zoo easily _____ to their new environment.
   Ⓐ **abrupted**   Ⓑ **admitted**   Ⓒ **adapted**   Ⓓ **abstained**

14 Mark Rothko is a famous _____ artist.
   Ⓐ **abstract**   Ⓑ **abstaining**   Ⓒ **adapted**   Ⓓ **absurd**

15 Luckily, my favorite fast food chain is _____ to the grocery store where we shop every week.
   Ⓐ **absorbed**   Ⓑ **adjacent**   Ⓒ **adhesive**   Ⓓ **adjourned**

More Prefixes and Suffixes © 2007 Creative Teaching Press

Word List: de-

de-	down, out

Vocabulary	**Definitions**
decay (v)	to break **down**; to rot
decline (v)	to go **down**; to droop; to slope **downward**
decode (v)	to break **down** words or sentences to read
decrease (v)	to lower or break **down** into a smaller amount
deduct (v)	to take **out**; to remove; to take away from another (usually related to money)
dejected (adj)	feeling **down**; sad
depress (v)	to press **down**
deport (v)	to send **out** of the country; to expel from the country

Vocabulary Sort: de-

Cut apart the words and definitions. Match each word to its definition. Check your answers by referring to the word list.

depress	**de**port	**de**duct	**de**jected
decode	**de**crease	**de**cline	**de**cay

to break **down** words or sentences to read	to send **out** of the country; to expel from the country
feeling **down**; sad	to press **down**
to lower or break **down** into a smaller amount	to take **out**; to remove; to take away from another (usually related to money)
to break **down**; to rot	to go **down**; to droop; to slope **downward**

Application and Practice: de-

Matching Clues to Vocabulary

Write the word that matches each clue.
Use each word only once.

deport	dejected	decrease	decay
depress	deduct	decode	decline

1 _____ The slope of the mountain made it difficult to climb down without slipping.

2 _____ She was learning how to break down multisyllabic words to help her read.

3 _____ He wants to lower his monthly expenses and bills.

4 _____ The tree was already beginning to rot after falling down in a storm.

5 _____ She needs to take out the money from her paycheck to pay her rent.

6 _____ You need to do this to the button so it will ring the bell.

7 _____ The man entered the United States illegally, so the authorities wanted to send him back to his native country.

8 _____ She felt so disappointed when her grandmother became too ill to visit.

Crossword Puzzle

Write the word that matches each clue to complete the puzzle.

Across

1. to send out of the country
2. feeling sad
4. to slope in a downward direction
5. to rot or break down naturally
6. to break down words in order to read

Down

1. to take out (often related to money)
3. to press down
4. to lower or break down into a smaller amount

More Prefixes and Suffixes © 2007 Creative Teaching Press

Read-Around Review: de-

I have the first card.

Who has the word that names what you do when you push **down** on something?

I have the word **decrease**.

Who has the word that describes the act of breaking **down** words into parts to read?

I have the word **depress**.

Who has the word that describes what is happening to a person when he or she is forced to leave the country?

I have the word **decode**.

Who has the word that describes the slope of a mountain as you ski **down** it?

I have the word **deport**.

Who has the word that describes when you are feeling very sad?

I have the word **decline**.

Who has the prefix that means **down** or **out**?

I have the word **dejected**.

Who has the word that describes what an adult might do when he or she has money taken **out** of a paycheck for future savings?

I have the prefix **de-**.

Who has the word that describes the breaking **down** of living things after they die?

I have the word **deduct**.

Who has the word that describes a change in temperature when it goes **down**?

I have the word **decay**.

Who has the first card?

More Prefixes and Suffixes © 2007 Creative Teaching Press

Name _____   Date _____

Vocabulary Quiz: de-

Shade in the bubble for the correct word.

1 The message was written backwards, so it was difficult for her to figure it out. What did she have to do?
   Ⓐ **deduct**   Ⓑ **deject**   Ⓒ **decay**   Ⓓ **decode**

2 The amount of homework near the end of the school year usually does this.
   Ⓐ **decodes**   Ⓑ **decreases**   Ⓒ **deducts**   Ⓓ **deports**

3 What could happen to a person from another country if he or she doesn't file the proper paperwork with the government? What might he or she be?
   Ⓐ **deported**   Ⓑ **decreased**   Ⓒ **deducted**   Ⓓ **declined**

4 You need to do this to the cut to make it stop bleeding.
   Ⓐ **deject**   Ⓑ **decode**   Ⓒ **depress**   Ⓓ **decay**

5 Martha was quite sad when she didn't get hired for the job. What was she?
   Ⓐ **dejected**   Ⓑ **decoded**   Ⓒ **deducted**   Ⓓ **deported**

6 Due to the way the street sloped downward, the water rushed by her house like a river during rainstorms. Which word describes the slope?
   Ⓐ **deduct**   Ⓑ **decline**   Ⓒ **decrease**   Ⓓ **depress**

7 To prevent tooth _____, it's important to brush and floss daily.
   Ⓐ **decrease**   Ⓑ **depress**   Ⓒ **decay**   Ⓓ **decode**

8 "I'm going to have to take $2.50 out of your allowance for not cleaning your room this week," said Teri. She had to _____ the money.
   Ⓐ **deduct**   Ⓑ **deject**   Ⓒ **deport**   Ⓓ **decline**

Write the correct form of the word on the line so the sentence makes sense and is grammatically correct.

9 I didn't mean to accidentally _____ that key on my computer!

10 Mara was feeling _____ after breaking her leg on her skateboard.

11 The government had to _____ the man because he was in the country illegally.

12 The roots of the plants were beginning to _____ after they were watered too much.

13 The weather forecaster said there is a _____ in the chance of rain over the weekend, so I might get to ride my bike to the park after all.

14 The _____ of the hill is too steep for me to run down so I will walk instead.

15 Before Sasha even sees her paycheck, her company will _____ the health insurance fee.

Word List: dif-, dis-, dys-

dif-, dis-, dys-	away, not, negative

Vocabulary	**Definitions**
differ (v)	to **not** agree; to have different ideas
differentiate (v)	to identify how things are **not** the same
disobey (v)	to **not** follow a rule or order
disagree (v)	to **not** share the same point of view
disconnect (v)	to take something apart so pieces are **not** attached
dismiss (v)	to send **away**
dispense (v)	to distribute; to send items **away** in groups
dysfunctional (adj)	**not** working properly

More Prefixes and Suffixes © 2007 Creative Teaching Press

Vocabulary Sort: dif-, dis-, dys-

Cut apart the words and definitions. Match each word to its definition. Check your answers by referring to the word list.

disobey	**dys**functional	**dis**pense	**dif**fer
dismiss	**dif**ferentiate	**dis**agree	**dis**connect

to send **away**	to **not** agree; to have different ideas
to identify how things are **not** the same	**not** working properly
to **not** share the same point of view	to take something apart so pieces are **not** attached
to distribute; to send items **away** in groups	to **not** follow a rule or order

Application and Practice: dif-, dis-, dys-

Sentence Fill-ins ···

Complete each sentence with the correct word. Use each word only once.

dispense	disobey	disconnect	differ
disagree	differentiate	dysfunctional	dismiss

1 The teacher was ready to _____ the class for lunch because they were sitting so quietly.

2 The candy machine can _____ three candies at a time for 25¢.

3 The lock was _____, so she threw the keys away.

4 The repairman had to _____ her air conditioning system and install a new one.

5 I must say that I _____ with your opinion, but I will respect your wishes.

6 I did not want to _____ my father because I knew that I would be grounded for the weekend.

7 Can you help me _____ between these two types of birds?

8 We clearly _____ in our paint color choices if I want blue and you want red.

Crossword Puzzle ···

Write the word that matches each clue to complete the puzzle.

Across
2. to send away
4. to have different ideas
7. not working properly

Down
1. to identify how things are not the same
3. to distribute
4. to make something not attached anymore
5. to not follow an order
6. to not share the same viewpoint

More Prefixes and Suffixes © 2007 Creative Teaching Press

Read-Around Review: dif-, dis-, dys-

I have the first card.

Who has the word that describes what you are doing when you have opposite points of view?

I have the word **dismiss**.

Who has the word that means to pass things out?

I have the word **disagree**.

Who has the word that describes what you do when you do **not** follow a rule?

I have the word **dispense**.

Who has the word that describes how two friends might **not** have the same ideas when planning for a weekend?

I have the word **disobey**.

Who has the word that means to identify how things are **not** the same?

I have the word **differ**.

Who has the word that describes something that is **not** working properly?

I have the word **differentiate**.

Who has the word that means to take something apart so it is **not** attached?

I have the word **dysfunctional**.

Who has the prefixes that mean **away**, **not**, or **negative**?

I have the word **disconnect**.

Who has the word that means to excuse someone and send them **away**?

I have the prefixes **dif-**, **dis-**, and **dys-**.

Who has the first card?

Vocabulary Quiz: dif-, dis, dys-

Shade in the bubble for the correct word.

1 If you help me figure out which pants are blue and which are black, what do we do?
    Ⓐ **differentiate**   Ⓑ **disobey**   Ⓒ **dispense**   Ⓓ **disagree**

2 You may not do this to the school rules or you may have to see the principal.
    Ⓐ **disconnect**   Ⓑ **dismiss**   Ⓒ **dysfunctional**   Ⓓ **disobey**

3 Which word describes what two family members do when they argue?
    Ⓐ **dispense**   Ⓑ **disagree**   Ⓒ **dismiss**   Ⓓ **differentiate**

4 Abby loves collecting the little candy containers that do this to one rectangular candy at a time.
    Ⓐ **disobey**   Ⓑ **dismiss**   Ⓒ **dispense**   Ⓓ **differentiate**

5 It was a hot day in Room 11 when the air conditioner stopped working. What was the air conditioner?
    Ⓐ **dysfunctional**   Ⓑ **dismissed**   Ⓒ **differentiated**   Ⓓ **dispensed**

6 Kellie and Bob were doing this when it came to naming their new puppy.
    Ⓐ **disconnecting**   Ⓑ **differing**   Ⓒ **differentiating**   Ⓓ **dispensing**

7 Will you please help me do this to the computer, so I can take it to the repair shop?
    Ⓐ **dismiss**   Ⓑ **differ**   Ⓒ **disagree**   Ⓓ **disconnect**

8 The teachers were released to go home after the staff meeting. What were they?
    Ⓐ **dismissed**   Ⓑ **differing**   Ⓒ **dysfunctional**   Ⓓ **disobey**

Write the correct form of the word on the line so the sentence makes sense and is grammatically correct.

9 Even the best of friends will sometimes _____ in their opinions.

10 The students were _____ early on the last day of school.

11 The teacher asked the student to _____ the papers in groups of three to the rest of the class.

12 The radio had to be exchanged because it was _____.

13 I can't _____ between the two voices on the phone because they sound so similar.

14 I was shocked to see the girl _____ her mother in the store!

15 Nina and Rex _____ on which television show to watch before bedtime.

More Prefixes and Suffixes © 2007 Creative Teaching Press

Name _____ Date _____

Review Test: de- and dif-, dis-, dys-

Shade in the bubble for the correct word.

1. Just _____ the fee from the money I owe you.
   Ⓐ **dispense** Ⓑ **differentiate** Ⓒ **deport** Ⓓ **deduct**

2. I don't find it fun to _____ because I do not like being in trouble!
   Ⓐ **dismiss** Ⓑ **disobey** Ⓒ **decline** Ⓓ **differ**

3. My sister and I often _____, but we still love each other.
   Ⓐ **decline** Ⓑ **disagree** Ⓒ **dismiss** Ⓓ **depress**

4. The twins looked so much alike that it was hard to _____ between them.
   Ⓐ **differentiate** Ⓑ **dismiss** Ⓒ **depress** Ⓓ **deport**

5. She broke her wrist after falling down the steep _____ of the hillside.
   Ⓐ **deduction** Ⓑ **deport** Ⓒ **disconnection** Ⓓ **decline**

6. Jake's tutor was helping him _____ the book so he would be able to read it.
   Ⓐ **dispense** Ⓑ **dismiss** Ⓒ **depress** Ⓓ **decode**

7. She was happy to notice a _____ in the amount of time it took Joseph to get ready in the morning.
   Ⓐ **decrease** Ⓑ **decay** Ⓒ **dismissal** Ⓓ **deduction**

8. It is possible for a fingernail infection to cause the nail to _____ and fall off.
   Ⓐ **deject** Ⓑ **dispense** Ⓒ **decay** Ⓓ **decline**

9. You need to _____ the hose from the dryer before cleaning out the lint.
   Ⓐ **disconnect** Ⓑ **depress** Ⓒ **differ** Ⓓ **dispense**

10. The _____ fan was returned to the manufacturer.
    Ⓐ **dysfunctional** Ⓑ **deducted** Ⓒ **differing** Ⓓ **depressed**

11. "You are now _____ to go home for the holidays," said Mr. Parker.
    Ⓐ **dispensed** Ⓑ **dysfunctional** Ⓒ **depressed** Ⓓ **dismissed**

12. The candy machine did not _____ the correct amount of change.
    Ⓐ **disconnect** Ⓑ **deport** Ⓒ **depress** Ⓓ **dispense**

13. We _____ in our opinions on who would make the best president.
    Ⓐ **differ** Ⓑ **decline** Ⓒ **dismiss** Ⓓ **decrease**

14. I can't believe that my mom _____ the end button in the middle of my phone call!
    Ⓐ **differed** Ⓑ **declined** Ⓒ **depressed** Ⓓ **decreased**

15. Zoé was feeling _____ as a result of being put on restriction.
    Ⓐ **disobeyed** Ⓑ **dejected** Ⓒ **dismissed** Ⓓ **deducted**

Word List: equ-, equi-

| equ-, equi- | equal, same |

Vocabulary	Definitions
equal (adj)	having the **same** measure, quantity, or number
equate (v)	to make **equal**; to make the **same** in amount
equation (n)	a mathematical formula for making different sets of numbers **equal**
equator (n)	imaginary line dividing the northern and southern hemispheres into **equal** parts; imaginary line around Earth that is **equally** distant from the poles
equiangular (adj)	having all angles **equal** in size
equilateral (adj)	having all sides **equal** in length
equinox (n)	one of two times a year when the day and night are nearly **equal** in length
equivalent (adj)	having the **same** amount; **equal** in force or value

More Prefixes and Suffixes © 2007 Creative Teaching Press

Vocabulary Sort: equ-, equi-

Cut apart the words and definitions. Match each word to its definition. Check your answers by referring to the word list.

equivalent	**equ**ate	**equ**ator	**equ**inox
equiangular	**equ**al	**equ**ation	**equi**lateral

having all angles **equal** in size	having the **same** measure, quantity, or number
a mathematical formula for making different sets of numbers **equal**	imaginary line dividing the northern and southern hemispheres into **equal** parts; imaginary line around Earth that is **equally** distant from the poles
having the **same** amount; **equal** in force or value	to make **equal**; to make the **same** in amount
having all sides **equal** in length	one of two times a year when the day and night are nearly **equal** in length

Application and Practice: equ-, equi-

Matching Clues to Vocabulary ·

Write the word that matches each clue.
Use each word only once.

| equation | equiangular | equinox | equate |
| equator | equivalent | equilateral | equal |

1 _____ The angles of the triangle were exactly the same. What were the angles?

2 _____ This point on Earth has higher temperatures because it's the farthest from the poles. What is this point called?

3 _____ Jon complained that he only got half of the candy bar while Simon got three out of six pieces. Simon said that the two amounts were what to one another?

4 _____ When day and night are of equal lengths, it is called this.

5 _____ Have you figured out the formula to that math problem?

6 _____ Squares that have the same-sized sides and are called this.

7 _____ The girls always received the same number of gifts each year.

8 _____ Please figure out a way to make these two sides of the equation equal.

Crossword Puzzle ·

Write the word that matches each clue to complete the puzzle.

Across
2. the same measure
5. to make even
8. the angles are all the same size

Down
1. sides with the same length
3. equal in force or value
4. the imaginary line around the Earth
6. a math problem in which both sides are the same
7. day and night are of equal length on this day

Read-Around Review: equ-, equi-

I have the first card.

Who has the word that describes an object with sides of **equal** lengths?

I have the word **equation**.

Who has the word that means to make things **equal**, such as when you make two **equal** groups of candy?

I have the word **equilateral**.

Who has the word that names a day of the year in which day and night are nearly **equal** in length?

I have the word **equate**.

Who has the word that means the **same** quantity, such as when you compare 7 × 5 and 35?

I have the word **equinox**.

Who has the word that describes two things that have the same amount and are **equal** in force or value?

I have the word **equal**.

Who has the word that describes shapes that have **equally**-sized angles?

I have the word **equivalent**.

Who has the prefixes that mean **equal** or **same**?

I have the word **equiangular**.

Who has the word that names the imaginary line around the center of the Earth in which the warmest temperatures are usually found?

I have the prefixes **equ-** and **equi-**.

Who has the word that names the kind of math problems you solve every day?

I have the word **equator**.

Who has the first card?

Vocabulary Quiz: equ-, equi-

Shade in the bubble for the correct word.

1 "I am going to give each of you the same amount of allowance," said Rick.
Ⓐ **equation**   Ⓑ **equiangular**   Ⓒ **equilateral**   Ⓓ **equivalent**

2 "In two days, we will enjoy a day in which day and night are almost equal," said Mr. Nguyen.
Ⓐ **equinox**   Ⓑ **equilateral**   Ⓒ **equation**   Ⓓ **equator**

3 Your homework tonight is to create three different shapes on which all sides are equal.
Ⓐ **equal**   Ⓑ **equiangular**   Ⓒ **equilateral**   Ⓓ **equinox**

4 Ecuador, Kenya, and Gabon are directly on this part of the globe, so the weather is usually quite hot.
Ⓐ **equinox**   Ⓑ **equator**   Ⓒ **equivalent**   Ⓓ **equilateral**

5 Please solve this problem using two different strategies or formulas.
Ⓐ **equate**   Ⓑ **equinox**   Ⓒ **equiangular**   Ⓓ **equation**

6 The angles on this rectangle are all the same.
Ⓐ **equiangular**   Ⓑ **equilateral**   Ⓒ **equinox**   Ⓓ **equation**

7 Your task is to figure out a way to make these two plates of cookies even. What do you have to do to them?
Ⓐ **equinox**   Ⓑ **equilateral**   Ⓒ **equate**   Ⓓ **equiangular**

8 The distance from your house to school is the same as the distance from your house to the market. What are the distances?
Ⓐ **equiangular**   Ⓑ **equations**   Ⓒ **equal**   Ⓓ **equinoxes**

Write the correct form of the word on the line so the sentence makes sense and is grammatically correct.

9 Let's make sure to _____ the number of cookies each student receives.

10 The answer to that _____ is 64.

11 I know that 9×9 is _____ to 27×3.

12 A square is always _____ and _____.

13 My brother and I have _____ amounts of homework.

14 The Autumnal _____ in 2020 will be on September 22nd.

15 Countries that are nearest to the _____ have the quickest sunrises and sunsets.

More Prefixes and Suffixes © 2007 Creative Teaching Press

Word List: hemi-, semi-

hemi-, semi-	half, halfway

Vocabulary	Definitions
hemisphere (n)	one-**half** of the Earth as divided by the equator
semiannual (adj)	occurring twice a year; happening once every **half** year
semiarid (adj)	relating to a **halfway** dry region; somewhat arid; having little annual rainfall
semicircle (n)	a **half** circle
semiconscious (adj)	**halfway** conscious; not completely aware of sensations
semiformal (adj)	**halfway** between casual and formal in dress
semisweet (adj)	**halfway** between bitter and sweet; partly sweet
semiweekly (adj)	occurring twice a week; once every **half** week

Vocabulary Sort: hemi-, semi-

Cut apart the words and definitions. Match each word to its definition. Check your answers by referring to the word list.

semicircle	**hemi**sphere	**semi**conscious	**semi**weekly
semiannual	**semi**formal	**semi**sweet	**semi**arid

halfway between casual and formal in dress	**halfway** between bitter and sweet; partly sweet
occurring twice a year; happening once every **half** year	one-**half** of the Earth as divided by the equator
halfway conscious; not completely aware of sensations	occurring twice a week; once every **half** week
relating to a **halfway** dry region; somewhat arid; having little annual rainfall	a **half** circle

More Prefixes and Suffixes © 2007 Creative Teaching Press

Application and Practice: hemi-, semi-

Sentence Fill-ins

Complete each sentence with the correct word. Use each word only once.

semicircle	semiweekly	semiannual	semiformal
semiarid	hemisphere	semiconscious	semisweet

1. Australia is located in the Southern _____ below the equator.

2. My favorite store only has its famous _____ sale twice a year.

3. Billy lives in a _____ state with little annual rainfall.

4. After he hit his head in the accident, Jermaine was only _____.

5. Franklin wore a dinner jacket and Erin wore a fancy black dress to the _____ party.

6. Do these cookies have _____ chocolate chips in them?

7. Joey is such a great artist that he can draw any animal out of the shape of a _____.

8. Elliot's mom volunteers in class on a _____ basis, so he sees her twice a week at school.

Crossword Puzzle

Write the word that matches each clue to complete the puzzle.

Across

1. describes a partly dry region that receives little rainfall each year
2. occurring twice a week
4. half of a circle
5. describes food items that taste partly sweet
6. one-half of the Earth
7. describes clothing halfway between casual and very dressy

Down

1. only halfway alert and aware of the senses
3. something that happens twice a year

Read-Around Review: hemi-, semi-

I have the first card.

Who has the prefixes that mean **half** or **halfway**?

I have the word **semisweet**.

Who has the word that names the face of the shape of an orange if you cut it in **half**?

I have the prefixes **hemi-** and **semi-**.

Who has the word that describes an area on Earth that receives little rainfall each year?

I have the word **semicircle**.

Who has the word that describes how often an event takes place if it is twice a week?

I have the word **semiarid**.

Who has the word that describes a person who has just come out of surgery and is **halfway** aware of what is around him or her?

I have the word **semiweekly**.

Who has the word that names one-**half** of the Earth?

I have the word **semiconscious**.

Who has the word that describes the expected dress code at many events such as museum openings, special occasions, and Broadway shows?

I have the word **hemisphere**.

Who has the word that describes how often an event takes place if it is twice a year?

I have the word **semiformal**.

Who has the word that describes food that tastes a bit sweet and a bit bitter at the same time?

I have the word **semiannual**.

Who has the first card?

Name _____ Date _____

Vocabulary Quiz: hemi-, semi-

Shade in the bubble for the correct word.

1 Lucas lives in Canada, which is in the northern _____ of Earth.
Ⓐ **semiannual**　　Ⓑ **hemisphere**　　Ⓒ **semicircle**　　Ⓓ **semiarid**

2 My school has a _____ bake sale in October and April of each school year.
Ⓐ **semiweekly**　　Ⓑ **semiformal**　　Ⓒ **semisweet**　　Ⓓ **semiannual**

3 This describes two major deserts in the United States. They include the Great Basin and sagebrush regions of Utah and Montana. Their climates are _____.
Ⓐ **semiannual**　　Ⓑ **hemisphere**　　Ⓒ **semiarid**　　Ⓓ **semisweet**

4 To begin the project, she cut the paper plate into two halves. What are the halves called?
Ⓐ **hemispheres**　　Ⓑ **semicircles**　　Ⓒ **semiformal**　　Ⓓ **semisweet**

5 She was _____ of her surroundings when the alarm went off at midnight because she was still partly asleep.
Ⓐ **semiconscious**　　Ⓑ **semiarid**　　Ⓒ **semisweet**　　Ⓓ **semiannual**

6 I made some delicious chocolate brownies for the picnic. What could they have been?
Ⓐ **semiarid**　　Ⓑ **semiformal**　　Ⓒ **semiannual**　　Ⓓ **semisweet**

7 The invitation stated that the attire should be fancy with black as the best color. What kind of attire is this?
Ⓐ **semiannual**　　Ⓑ **semiarid**　　Ⓒ **semiformal**　　Ⓓ **semiconscious**

8 Megan works with a tutor twice a week. She sees the tutor _____.
Ⓐ **semiweekly**　　Ⓑ **semiconscious**　　Ⓒ **semiannual**　　Ⓓ **semiarid**

Write the correct form of the word on the line so the sentence makes sense and is grammatically correct.

9 The secret to her muffins was adding a few _____ chocolate chunks to the mix.

10 We go to music class on a _____ basis, and gym class on the other three days.

11 Countries near the equator are sometimes considered to be in both the Northern and Southern _____.

12 Weaver School's _____ Ice Cream Social occurs in September and March.

13 The airplane flew in the shape of a _____ over the ocean.

14 Lucinda was awakened suddenly and was having trouble thinking. She was _____.

15 Please remember to wear _____ clothing to the dance Saturday night.

More Prefixes and Suffixes © 2007 Creative Teaching Press

Review Test: equ-, equi- and hemi-, semi-

Shade in the bubble for the correct word.

1 Aaron was an amazing mathematician. What could he solve in his head?
   Ⓐ **equators**   Ⓑ **equations**   Ⓒ **equilaterals**   Ⓓ **semicircles**

2 Her candy bar was made out of which type of chocolate?
   Ⓐ **semiarid**   Ⓑ **semicircular**   Ⓒ **semiformal**   Ⓓ **semisweet**

3 Jackie is lucky enough to have her housekeeper come twice a week to clean! How often is this?
   Ⓐ **semiweekly**   Ⓑ **semiannually**   Ⓒ **equates**   Ⓓ **semiformal**

4 My part of the lunch bill comes to $12.00 including the tip, which _____ to about half of the bill.
   Ⓐ **equates**   Ⓑ **semicircles**   Ⓒ **semiconscious**   Ⓓ **equiangular**

5 The zoo only offers the overnight camping experience twice a year. How often is this?
   Ⓐ **semiarid**   Ⓑ **semiweekly**   Ⓒ **equivalent**   Ⓓ **semiannually**

6 This is the dividing line between the Northern and Southern Hemispheres.
   Ⓐ **hemisphere**   Ⓑ **equinox**   Ⓒ **equator**   Ⓓ **semiarid**

7 About one-half of the state of Arizona is considered to have this climate.
   Ⓐ **semiarid**   Ⓑ **semiconscious**   Ⓒ **equiangular**   Ⓓ **semiformal**

8 This is the day in which day and night are of nearly equal length.
   Ⓐ **equivalent**   Ⓑ **equate**   Ⓒ **hemisphere**   Ⓓ **equinox**

9 A report card of straight A's is the same as a 4.0 grade point average because they are _____.
   Ⓐ **equivalent**   Ⓑ **semiformal**   Ⓒ **semiarid**   Ⓓ **equilateral**

10 All of the horses at the ranch are treated with _____ amounts of care and love.
   Ⓐ **semiconscious** Ⓑ **equate**   Ⓒ **equal**   Ⓓ **equilateral**

11 If you cut a tortilla in half, what shape will you have?
   Ⓐ **semicircle**   Ⓑ **hemisphere**   Ⓒ **semiconscious**   Ⓓ **equiangular**

12 She was only somewhat alert after having her tonsils removed by the doctor. She was _____.
   Ⓐ **semiconscious** Ⓑ **equivalent**   Ⓒ **semiformal**   Ⓓ **semiarid**

13 These parts of the Earth can be split into northern and southern or eastern and western.
   Ⓐ **semiarid**   Ⓑ **equations**   Ⓒ **hemispheres**   Ⓓ **equators**

14 How could you describe the sides of a regular hexagon?
   Ⓐ **equiangular**   Ⓑ **semicircular**   Ⓒ **equilateral**   Ⓓ **equators**

15 If you measured the degrees of the angles of a regular pentagon, you would discover that they are what?
   Ⓐ **equiangular**   Ⓑ **semicircles**   Ⓒ **semiarid**   Ⓓ **equators**

Word List: cent-, centi-, dec-, deca-

cent-, centi- dec-, deca-	hundred ten

Vocabulary	**Definitions**
centennial (adj)	an event that occurs every **100** years; a **100**th anniversary
centimeter (n)	a unit of length in the metric system; it takes **100** to equal 1 meter
centipede (n)	an arthropod with perhaps **100** legs
century (n)	a period of **100** years
decade (n)	a period of **ten** years
decagon (n)	a polygon with **ten** sides and **ten** angles
decathlon (n)	an athletic contest consisting of **ten** different events
decimal (n)	a number using the base of **ten**; a part of a whole based on groups of **ten**

Vocabulary Sort: cent-, centi-, dec-, deca-

Cut apart the words and definitions. Match each word to its definition. Check your answers by referring to the word list.

century	**deca**gon	**centi**meter	**dec**imal
decade	**centi**pede	**deca**thlon	**cent**ennial

an athletic contest consisting of **ten** different events	a period of **100** years
a period of **ten** years	an arthropod with perhaps **100** legs
a polygon with **ten** sides and **ten** angles	an event that occurs every **100** years; a **100**th anniversary
a number using the base of **ten**; a part of a whole based on groups of **ten**	a unit of length in the metric system; it takes **100** to equal 1 meter

Name _____   Date _____

Application and Practice: cent-, centi-, dec-, deca-

Matching Clues to Vocabulary

Write the word that matches each clue.
Use each word only once.

decathlon	decade	centimeter	century
centennial	centipede	decimal	decagon

1 _____ The athletes were training for all ten events for an entire year.

2 _____ This creature can have a poisonous bite.

3 _____ You can write one of these to equal a fraction.

4 _____ It is extremely difficult to draw one of these polygons.

5 _____ Irene has celebrated the last ten birthdays with a themed party. How much time is this?

6 _____ Few people are lucky enough to celebrate their 100th birthday.

7 _____ When a country celebrates this anniversary, it's a grand sight to see.

8 _____ A centipede can travel as far as 50 of these in only one second!

Crossword Puzzle

Write the word that matches each clue to complete the puzzle.

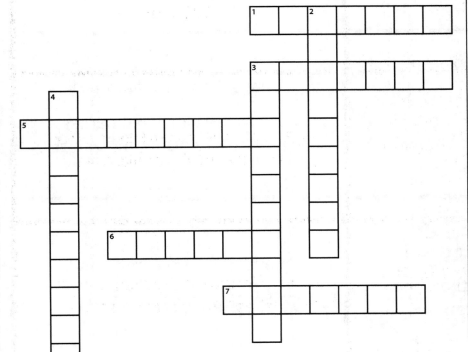

Across

1. a shape with ten sides and ten angles
3. 100 years
5. an athletic event that has ten different activities
6. 10 years
7. a part of a whole; a fraction; uses base ten

Down

2. a creature said to have 100 legs
3. a measurement on a ruler that is 1/100 of a meter
4. a celebration that occurs every 100 years

Read-Around Review: cent-, centi-, dec-, deca-

I have the first card.

Who has the word that names a period of **ten** years?

I have the prefixes **cent-, centi-** and **dec-, deca-**.

Who has the measurement that is 1/**100**th of a meter?

I have the word **decade**.

Who has the word that names a period of **100** years?

I have the word **centimeter**.

Who has the word that names the creature said to have **100** legs?

I have the word **century**.

Who has the word that names a shape with **ten** sides and **ten** angles?

I have the word **centipede**.

Who has the word that is equivalent to a fraction using the base **ten** system?

I have the word **decagon**.

Who has the word that names the contest athletes compete in which requires skill and training in **ten** events?

I have the word **decimal**.

Who has the word that names a celebration of a **100**th anniversary?

I have the word **decathlon**.

Who has the prefixes that mean **hundred** and **ten**?

I have the word **centennial**.

Who has the first card?

Name _____   Date _____

Vocabulary Quiz: cent-, centi-, dec-, deca-

Shade in the bubble for the correct word.

1 What is that creature? It has so many legs!
Ⓐ **centennial**　　Ⓑ **centipede**　　Ⓒ **decathlon**　　Ⓓ **decagon**

2 A house built in this shape is said to be able to withstand a hurricane better than a rectangular house.
Ⓐ **decade**　　Ⓑ **decathlon**　　Ⓒ **decagon**　　Ⓓ **centennial**

3 Her luggage was not even as wide as a full meter because it measured exactly 85 of these.
Ⓐ **centipedes**　　Ⓑ **decades**　　Ⓒ **centennials**　　Ⓓ **centimeters**

4 Can you believe that my dad is planning to compete in this annual event?
Ⓐ **decathlon**　　Ⓑ **centennial**　　Ⓒ **decagon**　　Ⓓ **century**

5 It's hard to believe, but she has lived in her house for ten years already. She has been there for a what?
Ⓐ **century**　　Ⓑ **decagon**　　Ⓒ **centennial**　　Ⓓ **decade**

6 Our money system requires you to write these when writing money amounts on paper.
Ⓐ **decathlons**　　Ⓑ **decimals**　　Ⓒ **centimeters**　　Ⓓ **decagons**

7 When a company celebrates this anniversary, it will be in the newspapers due to its rarity.
Ⓐ **decade**　　Ⓑ **century**　　Ⓒ **centennial**　　Ⓓ **decathlon**

8 Since my grandpa is 98 years old, he hopes to make it to this unique mark.
Ⓐ **century**　　Ⓑ **decade**　　Ⓒ **decagon**　　Ⓓ **centimeter**

Write the correct form of the word on the line so the sentence makes sense and is grammatically correct.

9 She wanted to have a _____ for a pet until she heard that it stings.

10 Please use the _____ side of the ruler to measure the length of your longest finger.

11 Her aunt is competing in the Long Island _____ next year.

12 Erika and her dad tried building the treehouse in the shape of a _____, but it turned out to be too difficult.

13 It's been two _____ since I've seen my cousin Rico. He was just a baby 21 years ago when I saw him.

14 I know that the _____ form of 3½ is 3.5.

15 The _____ celebration of the creation of the town hall was enjoyed by everyone!

Word List: penta-, oct-, sol-, soli-

penta-	five
oct-	eight
sol-, soli-	one, only, alone

Vocabulary	Definitions
pentagon (n)	a polygon with **five** sides and **five** angles
pentathlon (n)	an athletic contest consisting of **five** different events
octagon (n)	a shape with **eight** sides and **eight** angles
octave (n)	a group or series of **eight**; in music, a tone **eight** degrees higher or lower than another tone
octet (n)	a group of **eight**; **eight** musicians
octopus (n)	a mollusk with **eight** tentacles
solitaire (n)	a card game played by **one** person
solitude (n)	isolation; seclusion; the state of being **alone**

More Prefixes and Suffixes © 2007 Creative Teaching Press

Vocabulary Sort: penta-, oct-, sol-, soli-

Cut apart the words and definitions. Match each word to its definition. Check your answers by referring to the word list.

octopus	**oct**ave	**penta**thlon	**soli**tude
pentagon	**oct**et	**soli**taire	**oct**agon

a shape with **eight** sides and **eight** angles	a card game played by **one** person
a mollusk with **eight** tentacles	isolation; seclusion; the state of being **alone**
a group of **eight**; **eight** musicians	an athletic contest consisting of **five** different events
a polygon with **five** sides and **five** angles	a group or series of **eight**; in music, a tone **eight** degrees higher or lower than another tone

Application and Practice: penta-, oct-, sol-, soli-

Sentence Fill-ins

Complete each sentence with the correct word. Use each word only once.

| solitaire | octet | octagon | pentathlon |
| solitude | octave | pentagon | octopus |

1. My uncle is planning to compete in the upcoming _____.

2. Did you see the _____ while visiting the aquarium?

3. I just got a new deck of cards, so I'm ready to play _____.

4. The band consists of an _____, so they need a large stage.

5. She built a cabin in the unique shape of a _____ because her favorite number is five.

6. His music teacher was impressed with the _____ in which he could sing.

7. RaeAnn really needed some _____. She planned to spend the day in a quiet room reading a book to relax.

8. She bought a mirror that was in the eight-sided shape of an _____.

Crossword Puzzle

Write the word that matches each clue to complete the puzzle.

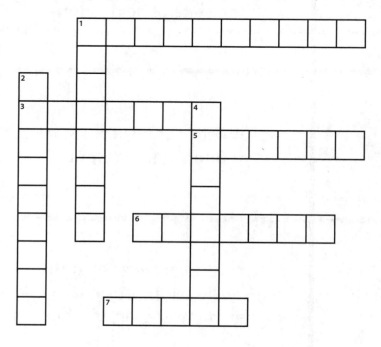

Across

1. an athletic contest with five different events
3. a mollusk with eight tentacles
5. a tone eight degrees higher or lower than another
6. a polygon with eight sides and eight angles
7. a group of eight musicians

Down

1. a polygon with five sides and five angles
2. a card game to play alone
4. a state of being alone

More Prefixes and Suffixes © 2007 Creative Teaching Press

Read-Around Review: penta-, oct-, sol-, soli-

I have the first card.

Who has the word that names a polygon with **five** sides and **five** angles?

I have the word **octet**.

Who has the word that identifies the musical word for **eight** degrees higher or lower in tone?

I have the word **pentagon**.

Who has the prefixes that mean **one**, **only**, or **alone**?

I have the word **octave**.

Who has the word that describes the state of being all **alone**?

I have the prefixes **sol-** and **soli-**.

Who has the word that names the card game you can play **alone**?

I have the word **solitude**.

Who has the word that names the competition involving **five** different events?

I have the word **solitaire**.

Who has the word that names a creature with **eight** tentacles?

I have the word **pentathlon**.

Who has the word that names a polygon with **eight** sides and **eight** angles?

I have the word **octopus**.

Who has the word that names a band with **eight** members?

I have the word **octagon**.

Who has the first card?

Name _____ Date _____

Vocabulary Quiz: penta-, oct-, sol-, soli-

Shade in the bubble for the correct word.

1 What is the name of the shape of a well-known, five-sided governmental building in the United States?
   Ⓐ **octagon**   Ⓑ **pentathlon**   Ⓒ **solitude**   Ⓓ **pentagon**

2 Grandma Dot taught her grandchildren how to play her favorite card game. What is the game?
   Ⓐ **solitaire**   Ⓑ **solitude**   Ⓒ **pentathlon**   Ⓓ **octave**

3 This creature has suction cups on every one of its eight tentacles.
   Ⓐ **octet**   Ⓑ **octave**   Ⓒ **octopus**   Ⓓ **octagon**

4 Lee Elementary School hired the eight famous members of the Jones Junction Band to play at their carnival. The eight-member group is called a what?
   Ⓐ **solitaire**   Ⓑ **octet**   Ⓒ **octave**   Ⓓ **pentathlon**

5 The members of the choir could sing in many different tone ranges. What are the tone ranges called?
   Ⓐ **octaves**   Ⓑ **octets**   Ⓒ **octagons**   Ⓓ **pentagons**

6 In early history, the events of this contest included discus, javelin, long jump, foot race, and wrestling.
   Ⓐ **pentathlon**   Ⓑ **pentagon**   Ⓒ **solitude**   Ⓓ **octave**

7 The unique shape of the table allowed for exactly eight dinner guests. What is the shape?
   Ⓐ **pentagon**   Ⓑ **octave**   Ⓒ **octet**   Ⓓ **octagon**

8 She was enjoying the peacefulness of walking on the beach alone. What is the word for this type of isolation?
   Ⓐ **solitaire**   Ⓑ **pentathlon**   Ⓒ **solitude**   Ⓓ **octave**

Write the correct form of the word on the line so the sentence makes sense and is grammatically correct.

9 If you stretched out two of its eight tentacles, the largest _____ would span over 8 feet wide.

10 There are _____ games with pegs as well as cards that you can play alone.

11 The eight members of the _____ were singing the best they ever had, each in a different _____.

12 A modern _____ includes five track and field events.

13 She went to the spa to relax alone in the hot steam room because she needed some _____.

14 The company tried to create a cereal with eight sides, but the _____ just looked like circles.

15 His new jigsaw puzzle had five edges instead of four; it was in the shape of a _____.

More Prefixes and Suffixes © 2007 Creative Teaching Press

Review Test: cent-, centi-, dec-, deca- and penta-, oct-, sol-, soli-

Shade in the bubble for the correct word.

1. Sarah has the most amazing voice. She can sing in a wide range of these.
   Ⓐ decades   Ⓑ octaves   Ⓒ octets   Ⓓ decades

2. At their _____ celebration, the farm released 100 butterflies to represent each year of operation.
   Ⓐ decade   Ⓑ pentagon   Ⓒ octagon   Ⓓ centennial

3. The _____ caught one of its eight tentacles on a piece of plastic litter.
   Ⓐ octopus   Ⓑ octet   Ⓒ decagon   Ⓓ octet

4. It had been 30 years since the last major flood in her town. That was three of *these*.
   Ⓐ decathlons   Ⓑ pentathlons   Ⓒ centuries   Ⓓ decades

5. For hundreds of years, scientists thought the bird was extinct until a few were discovered deep in the Brazilian rainforest. For how long did they think it was extinct?
   Ⓐ decades   Ⓑ centennials   Ⓒ centuries   Ⓓ octets

6. On Hudson's coffee table, there was a round wooden game with marbles that is played alone. What is the game called?
   Ⓐ decagon   Ⓑ solitaire   Ⓒ solitude   Ⓓ octave

7. That creature must have 100 legs! What is it?
   Ⓐ centimeter   Ⓑ centipede   Ⓒ octet   Ⓓ centennial

8. What is equivalent to a fraction?
   Ⓐ decimal   Ⓑ octave   Ⓒ decade   Ⓓ century

9. There are 100 of these in 1 meter.
   Ⓐ centuries   Ⓑ decades   Ⓒ centennials   Ⓓ centimeters

10. It's hard to find any time alone when you live in a house with twelve family members. What might be missing?
    Ⓐ centuries   Ⓑ centipedes   Ⓒ solitude   Ⓓ pentagons

11. This group of eight musicians was hired to play at the school dance.
    Ⓐ octet   Ⓑ octagons   Ⓒ solitaires   Ⓓ decades

12. Solve the analogy. *five* : _____ : : *six* : *hexagon*

13. Solve the analogy. *decathlon* : _____ : : *pentathlon* : *five*

14. Solve the analogy. *nonagon* : *nine* : : _____ : *ten*

15. Solve the analogy. *hexagon* : *six* : : _____ : *eight*

Word List: multi-

multi-	many

Vocabulary	Definitions
multicultural (adj)	relating to **many** different cultures
multilateral (adj)	having **many** different sides
multilingual (adj)	having the ability to speak **many** different languages
multimedia (adj)	combined use of **many** forms of communication and/or entertainment
multiply (v)	to increase in number; to make **many** of
multitude (n)	a large number of things; a group with **many** members
multiuse (adj)	having **many** uses
multivitamin (n)	a pill or tablet that includes **many** nutrients needed for health

Vocabulary Sort: multi-

Cut apart the words and definitions. Match each word to its definition. Check your answers by referring to the word list.

multitude	**multi**lateral	**multi**cultural	**multi**vitamin
multilingual	**multi**media	**multi**use	**multi**ply

combined use of **many** forms of communication and/or entertainment	relating to **many** different cultures
having **many** uses	to increase in number; to make **many** of
a large number of things; a group with **many** members	having **many** different sides
a pill or tablet that includes **many** nutrients needed for health	having the ability to speak **many** different languages

Application and Practice: multi-

Matching Clues to Vocabulary ·······················

Write the word that matches each clue.
Use each word only once.

multiuse	multilingual	multilateral	multiply
multitude	multimedia	multivitamin	multicultural

1 _____ Hampton is so creative with plastic bags! He finds many purposes for them around the house.

2 _____ Evan has so many pairs of shoes!

3 _____ I can do this to numbers in my head faster than anyone in my family.

4 _____ Sam's mom makes sure that he takes at least one of these each day so he grows up to be a healthy person.

5 _____ Nikolas can speak Spanish, English, French, and Portuguese.

6 _____ Kim comes from a heritage that includes Vietnamese, Dutch, and French ancestors.

7 _____ My homework was to create a many-sided figure out of toothpicks and peas.

8 _____ The presentation included video, photographs, newspaper articles, and music.

Crossword Puzzle ····································

Write the word that matches each clue to complete the puzzle.

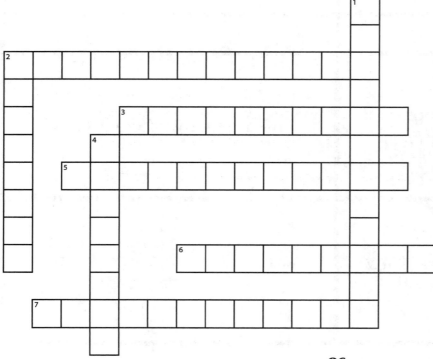

Across

2. relating to many different cultures
3. including many different forms of communication and entertainment
5. a pill that includes many nutrients needed by the body
6. a large amount
7. having many different sides

Down

1. able to speak many different languages
2. able to serve many functions
4. to increase the number of something many times

Read-Around Review: multi-

I have the first card.

Who has the word that describes content that can be communicated in **many** different forms?

I have the prefix **multi-**.

Who has the word that names a pill with **many** nutrients that contribute to good health?

I have the word **multimedia**.

Who has the word that means to increase in number **many** times?

I have the word **multivitamin**.

Who has the word that describes an object with **many** sides?

I have the word **multiply**.

Who has the word that means **many** things?

I have the word **multilateral**.

Who has the word that describes a person who speaks **many** different languages?

I have the word **multitude**.

Who has the word that describes something that serves **many** different purposes?

I have the word **multilingual**.

Who has the word that describes a feast having food and decorations from **many** different countries?

I have the word **multiuse**.

Who has the prefix that means **many**?

I have the word **multicultural**.

Who has the first card?

More Prefixes and Suffixes © 2007 Creative Teaching Press

Name _____   Date _____

Vocabulary Quiz: multi-

Shade in the bubble for the correct word.

1 What pill can be taken as an all-in-one tablet for good health?
    Ⓐ **multimedia**   Ⓑ **multicultural**   Ⓒ **multiuse**   Ⓓ **multivitamin**

2 Efren's new cell phone can be used to take pictures, record his voice, send text messages, and download television shows. What is it?
    Ⓐ **multilingual**   Ⓑ **multitude**   Ⓒ **multicultural**   Ⓓ **multiuse**

3 Kendra is a whiz at math just like her mom. They can do this easily in their heads!
    Ⓐ **multiply**   Ⓑ **multiuse**   Ⓒ **multimedia**   Ⓓ **multicultural**

4 Ian couldn't decide on a topping for his ice cream. There were too many to choose from.
    Ⓐ **multiuse**   Ⓑ **multitude**   Ⓒ **multimedia**   Ⓓ **multicultural**

5 Mr. Penner loved reading these types of books to his students so they would appreciate all people and lifestyles around the world.
    Ⓐ **multilateral**   Ⓑ **multimedia**   Ⓒ **multicultural**   Ⓓ **multilingual**

6 Elle can speak French, Cantonese, English, and Spanish. What is she?
    Ⓐ **multilateral**   Ⓑ **multicultural**   Ⓒ **multiuse**   Ⓓ **multilingual**

7 Maddox tried to make a sketch using only straight lines. The result was a mix of these shapes.
    Ⓐ **multiuse**   Ⓑ **multiplied**   Ⓒ **multilateral**   Ⓓ **multimedia**

8 Mrs. Chia bought a projector that connected to a computer, television, or PDA device.
    Ⓐ **multilateral**   Ⓑ **multimedia**   Ⓒ **multitude**   Ⓓ **multiply**

Write the correct form of the word on the line so the sentence makes sense and is grammatically correct.

9 Vincent was learning how to _____ any number by a two-digit number.

10 Sophia couldn't believe the _____ of baby chicks she saw in the room.

11 Her _____ radio included a flashlight, siren, and cell phone charger.

12 Nathaniel took his _____ every morning with breakfast to get his day off to a healthy start.

13 Some people have a talent for learning many languages, so they find it easy to become _____.

14 The United States is an example of a _____ land due to the various backgrounds of its people.

15 The Colby Corporation's annual meeting included a _____ presentation using video, speakerphones, and computers.

Word List: auto-, self-

| auto- | self |
| self- | self |

Vocabulary	Definitions
autobiography (n)	a book about a person's life written by him**self** or her**self**
autocrat (n)	a ruler with unlimited power; a person who rules by him**self** or her**self**
autograph (n)	the writing of one's own signature; the signature of one**self**
automatic (adj)	**self**-regulated; operated by it**self**
automobile (n)	a vehicle that can be operated by one**self**
autonomy (n)	governing over one**self**; free
self-sufficient (adj)	able to provide for the needs of one**self** without the help of others; independent
self-confident (adj)	feeling good about one**self**

Vocabulary Sort: auto-, self-

Cut apart the words and definitions. Match each word to its definition. Check your answers by referring to the word list.

self-sufficient	**auto**graph	**auto**crat	**auto**matic
automobile	**self**-confident	**auto**nomy	**auto**biography
self-regulated; operated by it**self**	able to provide for the needs of one**self** without the help of others; independent		
a vehicle that can be operated by one**self**	a ruler with unlimited power; a person who rules by him**self** or her**self**		
governing over one**self**; free	a book about a person's life written by him**self** or her**self**		
feeling good about one**self**	the writing of one's own signature; the signature of one**self**		

Name _____ Date _____

Application and Practice: auto-, self-

Sentence Fill-ins

Complete each sentence with the correct word. Use each word only once.

self-sufficient	automobile	autograph	autonomy
autobiography	self-confident	automatic	autocrat

1 Benji was reading the _____ of former President Bill Clinton's life.

2 A dictator could also be called an _____.

3 Becca was so excited when she got the _____ of her favorite singer!

4 People who are _____ don't wait for others to do things for them.

5 He didn't have to make the coffee because it was an _____ machine.

6 People can never live with complete _____ because there are always rules to follow.

7 Even though William couldn't sing well, he acted _____ during his performance.

8 Leah is looking for a new _____ that has leather seats and a sunroof.

Crossword Puzzle

Write the word that matches each clue to complete the puzzle.

Across

4. independent
5. complete freedom; making your own decisions
7. a person's signature
8. a vehicle that a person operates by him- or herself

Down

1. having positive feelings about yourself
2. a self-written book about one's life
3. happens without effort
6. a person who rules alone and has complete power

Read-Around Review: auto-, self-

I have the first card.

Who has the word that describes a person who feels positively about him**self** or her**self**?

I have the word **autonomy**.

Who has the word that describes the character trait of someone who can do things for him**self** or her**self**?

I have the word **self-confident**.

Who has the word that names the signature you might want to get if you see someone famous?

I have the word **self-sufficient**.

Who has the word that names the vehicle driven only by one**self**?

I have the word **autograph**.

Who has the word that describes something that happens without any thinking or effort on your part?

I have the word **automobile**.

Who has the word that names a ruler who enjoys complete power?

I have the word **automatic**.

Who has the prefixes that mean **self**?

I have the word **autocrat**.

Who has the word that names a book that was written by the person him**self** or her**self**?

I have the prefixes **auto-** and **self-**.

Who has the word that names what you have if you can make every decision freely your**self**?

I have the word **autobiography**.

Who has the first card?

More Prefixes and Suffixes © 2007 Creative Teaching Press

Name _____   Date _____

Vocabulary Quiz: auto-, self-

Shade in the bubble for the correct word.

1 Jan needed a car to get to work. What did she need?
Ⓐ **self-confident**   Ⓑ **autocrat**   Ⓒ **automobile**   Ⓓ **automatic**

2 Mason loved the freedom he had to do whatever he wanted on his weekends alone. This freedom is also called what?
Ⓐ **autonomy**   Ⓑ **automatic**   Ⓒ **autograph**   Ⓓ **autocrat**

3 Mia reminded Jack that he needed to be more independent. What did Jack need to be?
Ⓐ **autonomy**   Ⓑ **self-confident**   Ⓒ **autocrat**   Ⓓ **self-sufficient**

4 Jordan was thrilled to get the signature of her favorite surfing legend. What did she get?
Ⓐ **autograph**   Ⓑ **autonomy**   Ⓒ **automobile**   Ⓓ **automatic**

5 Many famous people have been known to write one of these. What is it called?
Ⓐ **autobiography**   Ⓑ **autocrat**   Ⓒ **autonomy**   Ⓓ **automobile**

6 That historical figure was known as one of the rulers who had unlimited power. What kind of ruler was he?
Ⓐ **autonomy**   Ⓑ **autograph**   Ⓒ **autobiography**   Ⓓ **autocrat**

7 She bought a cell phone with a voice message system that turned on by itself. What was the cell phone?
Ⓐ **automatic**   Ⓑ **self-sufficient**   Ⓒ **autocrat**   Ⓓ **self-confident**

8 Sari was sure that she would earn an A on the test because she knew the material so well. How did she feel?
Ⓐ **automobile**   Ⓑ **self-confident**   Ⓒ **self-sufficient**   Ⓓ **autonomy**

Write the correct form of the word on the line so the sentence makes sense and is grammatically correct.

9 You are being _____ by not asking for help from your parents.

10 The _____ salesman said the car could almost drive itself.

11 She bought an _____ garage door opener when she got tired of getting out to open the door in the rain.

12 Have you read the new _____ by Bill Gates?

13 If you believe in yourself, then you are _____.

14 I wish that I had more _____, as I would like to make more of my own decisions.

15 Did you really get that movie star's _____? Let me see it!

Review Test: multi- and auto-, self-

Shade in the bubble for the correct word.

1. Once an airplane is flying at a steady speed, it is often put in _____ pilot mode.
   - Ⓐ **multimedia**   Ⓑ **multilateral**   Ⓒ **automobile**   Ⓓ **automatic**

2. What do you call a tablet that you take daily for good health?
   - Ⓐ **autocrat**   Ⓑ **multivitamin**   Ⓒ **multilingual**   Ⓓ **autonomy**

3. What must you be if you want to go into international business or touring?
   - Ⓐ **autocrat**   Ⓑ **self-sufficient**   Ⓒ **multilingual**   Ⓓ **multimedia**

4. There are a _____ of different ways to solve a math problem.
   - Ⓐ **multitude**   Ⓑ **autonomy**   Ⓒ **multilateral**   Ⓓ **multiuse**

5. Suri was always doing things by herself without anyone's help. What was she being?
   - Ⓐ **autocrat**   Ⓑ **self-sufficient**   Ⓒ **multicultural**   Ⓓ **autonomy**

6. This is what you do when you make six groups of nine.
   - Ⓐ **multimedia**   Ⓑ **automatic**   Ⓒ **multilateral**   Ⓓ **multiply**

7. She started this type of campaign using computers, television, and radio ads when she decided to run for president.
   - Ⓐ **multilateral**   Ⓑ **autocratic**   Ⓒ **multiuse**   Ⓓ **multimedia**

8. Webster felt a certain amount of freedom in his sales job because he could make his own schedule every day. What was he exercising?
   - Ⓐ **multiuse**   Ⓑ **autocrat**   Ⓒ **autonomy**   Ⓓ **self-sufficient**

9. Debbie bought a new one of these when she decided she wanted to start a family.
   - Ⓐ **automobile**   Ⓑ **autograph**   Ⓒ **multiuse**   Ⓓ **multimedia**

10. Kimiko felt so good about herself that she didn't even care if her clothes matched. How was she feeling?
    - Ⓐ **self-sufficient**   Ⓑ **multilateral**   Ⓒ **self-confident**   Ⓓ **autocratic**

11. The auction site on the Internet was selling his signature for $45.00! What were they selling?
    - Ⓐ **autobiography**   Ⓑ **multicultural**   Ⓒ **multiuse**   Ⓓ **autograph**

12. The gym at her school was used for P.E., conferences, and lunch. It was a _____ room.
    - Ⓐ **multilateral**   Ⓑ **multiuse**   Ⓒ **multimedia**   Ⓓ **multicultural**

13. We live in a world full of different backgrounds, languages, and beliefs. Our world is what?
    - Ⓐ **multicultural**   Ⓑ **multilateral**   Ⓒ **self-sufficient**   Ⓓ **automatic**

14. Solve the analogy. *unilateral : one :: _____ : many*

15. Solve the analogy. *biography : someone else :: _____ : oneself*

More Prefixes and Suffixes © 2007 Creative Teaching Press

Word List: micro-

micro-	tiny, very small

Vocabulary	Definitions
microbiology (n)	the study of the **small**est forms of life such as bacteria, fungi, and viruses
microchip (n)	a **tiny** piece of a computer that holds the memory; a **tiny** piece of metal that has a memory and can be safely inserted into a pet for identification
microcosm (n)	a **tiny** world in comparison to a larger world
microfilm (n)	a material on which written forms are produced in **tiny** format for easier storage
microphone (n)	a device that converts **small** sounds into louder ones
microscope (n)	a tool that makes **tiny** objects appear much larger for close analysis
microscopic (adj)	describes something that is too **tiny** to see with the bare eye
microwave (n)	a device used to heat items in **small** amounts of time

More Prefixes and Suffixes © 2007 Creative Teaching Press

Vocabulary Sort: micro-

Cut apart the words and definitions. Match each word to its definition. Check your answers by referring to the word list.

microscope	**micro**chip	**micro**wave	**micro**cosm
microbiology	**micro**film	**micro**phone	**micro**scopic

describes something that is too **tiny** to see with the bare eye	the study of the **smallest** forms of life such as bacteria, fungi, and viruses
a device that converts **small** sounds into louder ones	a **tiny** piece of a computer that holds the memory; a **tiny** piece of metal that has a memory and can be safely inserted into a pet for identification
a device used to heat items in **small** amounts of time	a **tiny** world in comparison to a larger world
a tool that makes **tiny** objects appear much larger for close analysis	a material on which written forms are produced in **tiny** format for easier storage

More Prefixes and Suffixes © 2007 Creative Teaching Press

Application and Practice: micro-

Matching Clues to Vocabulary ······················

Write the word that matches each clue.
Use each word only once.

| microphone | microfilm | microwave | microcosm |
| microbiology | microchips | microscope | microscopic |

1 _____   Emma sang into this so that the entire audience could enjoy her beautiful voice.

2 _____   Dr. Harrison examined the liquid under this tool to see the particles.

3 _____   Tam could only cook using one of these machines. At least she never had to wait very long to eat.

4 _____   Libraries store old newspaper articles using this material.

5 _____   The computer company specialized in making these for increased memory in computer systems.

6 _____   If you compared your town to the entire world, it would be considered this.

7 _____   These particles are so small that they cannot be seen with your eyes alone.

8 _____   Marla wants to study this area of science in college.

Crossword Puzzle ·····························

Write the word that matches each clue to complete the puzzle.

Across

3. a tiny piece of a computer that holds the memory
4. a device that makes sounds louder
5. the study of the smallest forms of life
6. a tool that makes tiny objects appear larger

Down

1. something that is too tiny to see with the bare eye
2. a device used to heat food quickly
3. a tiny world compared to a larger world
4. a material that stores writing in a tiny format

Read-Around Review: micro-

I have the first card.

Who has the word that names the device used to make **small** sounds louder?

I have the word **microbiology**.

Who has the word that identifies a **tiny** world within a larger one?

I have the word **microphone**.

Who has the word that names the **tiny** format in which written material is stored in libraries so it doesn't take up much space?

I have the word **microcosm**.

Who has the prefix that means **tiny** or **very small**?

I have the word **microfilm**.

Who has the word that names the device used to heat soup faster than on a stove?

I have the prefix **micro-**.

Who has the word that describes the size of **tiny** things that the human eye cannot see?

I have the word **microwave**.

Who has the name of the **small** piece of metal in any computerized device that stores the data?

I have the word **microscopic**.

Who has the word that names the tool used to see **tiny** objects that would otherwise be invisible to the human eye?

I have the word **microchip**.

Who has the word that names the study of the **small**est forms of life?

I have the word **microscope**.

Who has the first card?

More Prefixes and Suffixes © 2007 Creative Teaching Press

Name _____ Date _____

Vocabulary Quiz: micro-

Shade in the bubble for the correct word.

1 Dr. MacDonald analyzed the skin using this tool.
    Ⓐ **microwave**   Ⓑ **microphone**   Ⓒ **microchip**   Ⓓ **microscope**

2 Miguel wants to study this field of science specializing in the smallest forms of life.
    Ⓐ **microbiology**   Ⓑ **microcosm**   Ⓒ **microwave**   Ⓓ **microfilm**

3 The world of ants is so tiny in comparison to the world of bugs. The world is called what?
    Ⓐ **microchip**   Ⓑ **microscopic**   Ⓒ **microcosm**   Ⓓ **microfilm**

4 You can project your voice by speaking into one of these when addressing a crowd.
    Ⓐ **microwave**   Ⓑ **microphone**   Ⓒ **microfilm**   Ⓓ **microcosm**

5 Larry was searching for a newspaper article from 1949 in the library. It was stored on this.
    Ⓐ **microfilm**   Ⓑ **microwave**   Ⓒ **microcosm**   Ⓓ **microbiology**

6 Every day, scientists are working on making smaller and smaller storage devices so the gadgets can also be smaller. These devices are called what?
    Ⓐ **microfilm**   Ⓑ **microcosm**   Ⓒ **microwaves**   Ⓓ **microchips**

7 The eggs of some insects are so tiny that you can't even see them. What are they?
    Ⓐ **microscopic**   Ⓑ **microwave**   Ⓒ **microfilm**   Ⓓ **microbiology**

8 Every morning, she made her hot chocolate in three minutes using this type of device.
    Ⓐ **microcosm**   Ⓑ **microbiology**   Ⓒ **microwave**   Ⓓ **microfilm**

Write the correct form of the word on the line so the sentence makes sense and is grammatically correct.

9 She became interested in _____ after learning about fungi and bacteria at Outdoor Science School.

10 The Kominsky family got a _____ for their new puppy, so he could be returned using the stored information if he was ever lost.

11 Where is my _____? I can't sing in the musical without it!

12 Scientists often use _____ to investigate tiny things in their laboratory.

13 Many libraries are beginning to store news data on DVD instead of _____.

14 Ellen's _____ broke, so she had to bake her potato in the oven.

15 The particles in the water were _____ so the man had no idea they were there.

Word List: mega-, megal-, megalo-

mega-, megal-, megalo-	large, great

Vocabulary	Definitions
megabyte (n)	a **large** unit of computer memory; one million bytes
megalith (n)	a very **large** stone used in prehistoric structures in Western Europe
megalomania (n)	a love of **great** things; an obsession with extravagant things
megalopolis (n)	a very **large** city; a very **large** region made up of many cities and towns
megaphone (n)	a funnel-shaped device used to make the voice **larger** (louder)
megalosaur (n)	a **large** dinosaur that lived during the Jurassic Period as a carnivore
megastar (n)	a very famous person; a **great** star
megavitamin (n)	a dose of a vitamin that provides a **larger** amount of nutrients than what is required to stay healthy

Vocabulary Sort: mega-, megal-, megalo-

Cut apart the words and definitions. Match each word to its definition. Check your answers by referring to the word list.

megalith	**megalo**saur	**mega**phone	**mega**byte
megalomania	**mega**star	**megalo**polis	**mega**vitamin

a very **large** city; a very **large** region made up of many cities and towns	a funnel-shaped device used to make the voice **larger** (louder)
a very famous person; a **great** star	a love of **great** things; an obsession with extravagant things
a **large** dinosaur that lived during the Jurassic Period as a carnivore	a very **large** stone used in prehistoric structures in Western Europe
a dose of a vitamin that provides a **large** amount more than what is required to stay healthy	a **large** unit of computer memory; one million bytes

Name _____   Date _____

Application and Practice: mega-, megal-, megalo-

Sentence Fill-ins

Complete each sentence with the correct word. Use each word only once.

megalith	megaphone	megalomania	megalopolis
megastar	megalosaur	megavitamin	megabytes

1. Lacey's new computer has 512 _____ of memory.

2. People who spend so much money on large, fancy things have _____.

3. Matia took a _____ because she thought she was catching a cold.

4. The cheerleading squad has a _____ so the crowd can hear their cheers.

5. Wyatt's dinosaur report was on the _____ that lived during the Jurassic Period.

6. Roberto moved to a small town in Kentucky, far away from the _____.

7. The singer was quickly becoming a _____ as a result of her number one hit single.

8. While on her European vacation, Tracie took pictures of a _____ that was hundreds of years old.

Crossword Puzzle

Write the word that matches each clue to complete the puzzle.

Across

5. an obsession with extravagant things
6. prehistoric stone structure in Western Europe
7. a very famous person
8. a funnel-shaped device that makes the voice louder

Down

1. a large carnivorous dinosaur
2. a large vitamin dose
3. a very large region made up of many cities and towns
4. a large unit of computer memory

More Prefixes and Suffixes © 2007 Creative Teaching Press

Read-Around Review: mega-, megal-, megalo-

I have the first card. Who has the word that names a **large** type of dinosaur that was a meat-eater during the Jurassic Period?	I have the word **megavitamin**. Who has the prefixes that mean **large** or **great**?
I have the word **megalosaur**. Who has the word that names a very **large** city or an area that includes many cities?	I have the prefixes **mega-**, **megal-**, and **megalo-**. Who has the word that names a **large** unit of computer memory?
I have the word **megalopolis**. Who has the word that names a deep love of fancy, extravagant, or **large** things?	I have the word **megabyte**. Who has the word that names a very **large** stone that was used in architecture in Western Europe many years ago?
I have the word **megalomania**. Who has the word that names a very famous person such as a singer or an actress?	I have the word **megalith**. Who has the word that names the funnel-shaped device used to make your voice sound louder?
I have the word **megastar**. Who has the word that names something a person might take that gives a **larger** amount of vitamins than needed for a healthy body?	I have the word **megaphone**. Who has the first card?

More Prefixes and Suffixes © 2007 Creative Teaching Press

Name _____ Date _____

Vocabulary Quiz: mega-, megal-, megalo-

Shade in the bubble for the correct word.

1 Fenton's photograph of the ancient stone structure built from these is hanging in his hallway.
   Ⓐ **megabytes**   Ⓑ **megastars**   Ⓒ **megaphones**   Ⓓ **megaliths**

2 The name of this extinct dinosaur means "big lizard."
   Ⓐ **megalosaur**   Ⓑ **megastar**   Ⓒ **megalopolis**   Ⓓ **megalith**

3 A popular home makeover show features the star yelling encouraging words into this device that makes his voice sound very loud.
   Ⓐ **megalith**   Ⓑ **megabyte**   Ⓒ **megastar**   Ⓓ **megaphone**

4 San Diego is quickly becoming one of these because there are so many small cities within the city limits.
   Ⓐ **megalopolis**   Ⓑ **megastar**   Ⓒ **megabyte**   Ⓓ **megaphone**

5 The units of memory in your computer are called what?
   Ⓐ **megaphones**   Ⓑ **megabytes**   Ⓒ **megastars**   Ⓓ **megalosaurs**

6 A person who has this obsession will spend all of his or her money on things rather than saving.
   Ⓐ **megalopolis**   Ⓑ **megastar**   Ⓒ **megalomania**   Ⓓ **megabyte**

7 Be careful when taking these because taking too much can actually make you sick instead of healthy.
   Ⓐ **megavitamins**   Ⓑ **megaliths**   Ⓒ **megabytes**   Ⓓ **megastars**

8 Jess thought he wanted to be one of these, but when it happened he was sad to find out that he couldn't even go to the store without being mobbed.
   Ⓐ **megalosaur**   Ⓑ **megastar**   Ⓒ **megabyte**   Ⓓ **megalomaniac**

Write the correct form of the word on the line so the sentence makes sense and is grammatically correct.

9 Many races begin with the announcer saying "On your mark, get set, go!" into a _____.

10 The _____ was a meat-eating biped who walked or ran on two legs during the Age of the Dinosaurs.

11 Who is your favorite _____ out of all the movie actors and actresses?

12 My mom took some _____ when she had a sore throat.

13 We need to buy a new computer with at least 256 _____ of memory.

14 I don't think I'm a _____ just because I love to buy expensive cars, jewelry, and coats!

15 Andy left his small town to attend college in a large, busy _____.

More Prefixes and Suffixes © 2007 Creative Teaching Press

Name _____ Date _____

Review Test: micro- and mega-, megal-, megalo-

Shade in the bubble for the correct word.

1. The speaker at the meeting needed to use one of these so the people in the back row could hear him.
   Ⓐ **megabyte**   Ⓑ **microphone**   Ⓒ **microscope**   Ⓓ **megalith**

2. She was so famous that people recognized her the minute she got off the plane in Africa. Many considered her a what?
   Ⓐ **microfilm**   Ⓑ **microcosm**   Ⓒ **megalith**   Ⓓ **megastar**

3. The doctor needed to analyze the tiny elements of bacteria that he couldn't see with his bare eyes because they were what?
   Ⓐ **megalosaurs**   Ⓑ **microcosms**   Ⓒ **microscopic**   Ⓓ **megalomaniacs**

4. These can make your voice sound louder to anyone listening.
   Ⓐ **megaphones**   Ⓑ **microfilms**   Ⓒ **megabytes**   Ⓓ **microcosms**

5. Scientists who study plants often look at these tiny worlds of life.
   Ⓐ **microcosms**   Ⓑ **megaliths**   Ⓒ **microfilms**   Ⓓ **megalomaniacs**

6. Libraries store many old articles from newspapers in this format, but they are currently changing to computer formats.
   Ⓐ **megabytes**   Ⓑ **microscopes**   Ⓒ **megaliths**   Ⓓ **microfilm**

7. I'm so lucky to have one of these because it makes my food cook faster.
   Ⓐ **megalopolis**   Ⓑ **megaphone**   Ⓒ **microscope**   Ⓓ **microwave**

8. This large, extinct, carnivorous reptile had two arms that were shorter than its legs.
   Ⓐ **megalosaur**   Ⓑ **microscopic**   Ⓒ **megalith**   Ⓓ **microbiology**

9. Many people who visit London, England try to visit Stonehenge. It's one of these famous stone structures.
   Ⓐ **megabytes**   Ⓑ **megaliths**   Ⓒ **microscopes**   Ⓓ **megaphones**

10. Dr. Naomi is famous for his knowledge in this field, especially on the topic of fungi.
    Ⓐ **megalomaniacs**   Ⓑ **microchips**   Ⓒ **megalosaurs**   Ⓓ **microbiology**

11. The need for these has increased each year as more people buy computers and need more memory.
    Ⓐ **microfilm**   Ⓑ **megavitamins**   Ⓒ **microchips**   Ⓓ **megaphones**

12. Do you live in a tiny town or one of these that's made up of many towns or cities?
    Ⓐ **microcosms**   Ⓑ **megalopolis**   Ⓒ **megabytes**   Ⓓ **microfilm**

13. Someone who spends excessive amounts of money on extravagant things could be called this.
    Ⓐ **megalomaniac**   Ⓑ **microcosm**   Ⓒ **microbiologist**   Ⓓ **megalosaur**

14. Solve the analogy.   *baby : stroller :: _____ : microchip*

15. Solve the analogy.   *telescope : far away things :: _____ : tiny things*

More Prefixes and Suffixes © 2007 Creative Teaching Press

Word List: -less

-less	without, lacking, not existing, not

Vocabulary	Definitions
care**less** (adj)	**without** a care; **lack** of thinking; **not** taking enough care in doing something
help**less** (adj)	**without** the ability to take action; powerless; **lacking** support or protection
home**less** (adj)	**lacking** a home or permanent place of residence
meaning**less** (adj)	**without** a purpose; **lacking** in importance; **not** important
pain**less** (adj)	**without** any uncomfortable feelings or complications
price**less** (adj)	**without** an exact value; of such worth that it can**not** be given a cost
rest**less** (adj)	unable to sit still or relax; **without** calm; busy
use**less** (adj)	**not** able to give service or aid; **lacking** use

More Prefixes and Suffixes © 2007 Creative Teaching Press

Vocabulary Sort: -less

Cut apart the words and definitions. Match each word to its definition. Check your answers by referring to the word list.

hel**ples**	price**less**	home**less**	use**less**
care**less**	rest**less**	meaning**less**	pain**less**

not able to give service or aid; **lacking** use	**without** an exact value; of such worth that it can**not** be given a cost
without any uncomfortable feelings or complications	**without** the ability to take action; powerless; **lacking** support or protection
unable to sit still or relax; **without** calm; busy	**without** a care; **lack** of thinking; **not** taking enough care in doing something
lacking a home or permanent place of residence	**without** a purpose; **lacking** in importance; **not** important

Application and Practice: -less

Matching Clues to Vocabulary ·······················

Write the word that matches each clue.
Use each word only once.

| meaningless | careless | restless | helpless |
| priceless | useless | homeless | painless |

1 _____ This word is often used to describe people who sleep on the streets or in their cars.

2 _____ I would never sell that vase because it belonged to my great-great grandmother.

3 _____ I just can't seem to relax! I think I'll go running along the beach.

4 _____ Zach felt this because he was unable to help the dying bird.

5 _____ A flashlight could be described as this if you try to use it without batteries.

6 _____ It was a waste of time to try and argue further with my friend. It was what?

7 _____ I made some silly mistakes in my report, and I didn't fix them before turning it in to my teacher. I was what?

8 _____ I couldn't believe that my dentist pulled a tooth, but I didn't feel a thing!

Crossword Puzzle ·······························

Write the word that matches each clue to complete the puzzle.

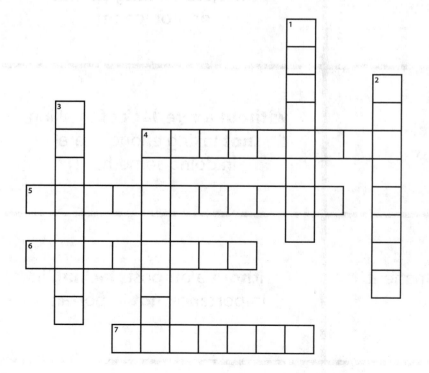

Across

4. without an exact value
5. lack of purpose
6. without the ability to take action or protest
7. not able to give service or aid

Down

1. lack of attention
2. always in motion
3. without a place of residence
4. without any sense of discomfort

More Prefixes and Suffixes © 2007 Creative Teaching Press

Read-Around Review: -less

I have the first card.

Who has the word that describes
a feeling of being unable to assist
or protect someone?

I have the word **homeless**.

Who has the word that describes
something that can**not** be
of any service or aid?

I have the word **helpless**.

Who has the word
that describes a **lack** of discomfort
or complications?

I have the word **useless**.

Who has the word that describes
a person who just can**not**
relax or stay still?

I have the word **painless**.

Who has the word that describes
something that is **not** important
and **lacks** a purpose?

I have the word **restless**.

Who has the word that describes
messy work in which a person
did **not** take his or her time?

I have the word **meaningless**.

Who has the word that describes
something so valuable that you
could never calculate its worth?

I have the word **careless**.

Who has the suffix that means
without, **lacking**, **not existing**,
or **not**?

I have the word **priceless**.

Who has the word that describes
a person **without** a place to live?

I have the suffix **-less**.

Who has the first card?

Name _____   Date _____

Vocabulary Quiz: -less

Shade in the bubble for the correct word.

1. Maya didn't know what to do! Her dog was obviously in pain, so she rushed him to the veterinarian. How did she feel?
   ⒜ careless   ⒝ homeless   ⒞ helpless   ⒟ priceless

2. The marker didn't work anymore because someone had left off the cap. What was it?
   ⒜ useless   ⒝ meaningless   ⒞ restless   ⒟ careless

3. Going to the dentist is now this because Dr. Phillips uses a new kind of drill.
   ⒜ meaningless   ⒝ painless   ⒞ restless   ⒟ homeless

4. Family heirlooms are worth more than any amount of money. Which word describes these items?
   ⒜ meaningless   ⒝ helpless   ⒞ careless   ⒟ priceless

5. Kyle just couldn't sit still in his seat. He kept thinking about the upcoming soccer game. What was he?
   ⒜ helpless   ⒝ restless   ⒞ meaningless   ⒟ careless

6. After the tornado blew their house away, the Greenes had to move into the high school gym until it could be rebuilt. What were they?
   ⒜ homeless   ⒝ useless   ⒞ helpless   ⒟ restless

7. Yesterday, Mike wrote a letter apologizing for teasing at school. Today, he was caught teasing again. What was his letter?
   ⒜ helpless   ⒝ homeless   ⒞ careless   ⒟ meaningless

8. It is John's job to double-check the newspaper for mistakes before it is printed. He can't be this.
   ⒜ painless   ⒝ helpless   ⒞ careless   ⒟ homeless

Write the correct form of the word on the line so the sentence makes sense and is grammatically correct.

9. Many adults believe that watching television or playing video games is _____.

10. The stray dog wandered around the city because it was _____.

11. Kim felt _____ when her newborn baby was crying, because she didn't know what he wanted.

12. What a _____ driver! He didn't use his turn signal and nearly caused an accident!

13. Many artifacts on display in museums are _____ and cannot be replaced.

14. Researchers and scientists are working hard to develop _____ ways to treat diseases.

15. After waiting in line for more than two hours, Joey was beginning to feel _____.

More Prefixes and Suffixes © 2007 Creative Teaching Press

Word List: -ness

-ness	the state, quality, or condition of something

Vocabulary	Definitions
bold**ness** (n)	**state of** being daring, brave, or courageous
clever**ness** (n)	**state of** being smart, bright, or imaginative
damp**ness** (n)	**state of** being a bit wet or moist
fond**ness** (n)	**state of** affection; liking something or someone
foolish**ness** (n)	**state of** being silly; lacking good sense or judgment
sad**ness** (n)	**state of** unhappiness; feeling sorrow; not in a **state of** well-being
sick**ness** (n)	**state of** illness
wilder**ness** (n)	an area with the **quality of** the untamed world; a large tract of land covered by dense forests

Vocabulary Sort: -ness

Cut apart the words and definitions. Match each word to its definition. Check your answers by referring to the word list.

foolish**ness**	clever**ness**	wilder**ness**	damp**ness**
sick**ness**	bold**ness**	fond**ness**	sad**ness**

state of being smart, bright, or imaginative	**state of** being daring, brave, or courageous
state of being silly; lacking good sense or judgment	an area with the **quality of** the untamed world; a large tract of land covered by dense forests
state of illness	**state of** unhappiness; feeling sorrow; not in a **state of** well-being
state of affection; liking something or someone	**state of** being a bit wet or moist

More Prefixes and Suffixes © 2007 Creative Teaching Press

Application and Practice: -ness

Sentence Fill-ins ··································

Complete each sentence with the correct
word. Use each word only once.

fondness	sickness	wilderness	foolishness
sadness	boldness	dampness	cleverness

1 Troop 24 was headed to the _____ for their annual camping trip.

2 She has a _____ for sweets, but her dentist said that it's damaging her teeth.

3 Myles told his son that the _____ needed to stop before he got hurt.

4 The _____ in the air signaled that rain was coming soon.

5 The fox's _____ was revealed through his smart ideas.

6 The _____ of color choices for her bedroom walls was shocking!

7 Tia felt a sense of _____ when she found out her friend was moving away.

8 Dr. Vu said that the _____ would spread to his classmates if Tim went to school.

Crossword Puzzle ··································

Write the word that matches each clue to complete the puzzle.

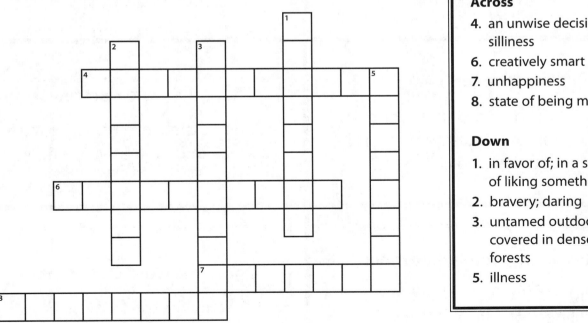

Across
4. an unwise decision; silliness
6. creatively smart
7. unhappiness
8. state of being moist

Down
1. in favor of; in a state of liking something
2. bravery; daring
3. untamed outdoors covered in dense forests
5. illness

More Prefixes and Suffixes © 2007 Creative Teaching Press

Read-Around Review: -ness

I have the first card.

Who has the word that names a feeling of being brave?

I have the word **foolishness**.

Who has the word that identifies a feeling of affection?

I have the word **boldness**.

Who has the word that identifies an unhappy feeling?

I have the word **fondness**.

Who has the word that identifies a **state of** unhealthiness or illness?

I have the word **sadness**.

Who has the suffix that means **the state**, **quality**, or **condition of something**?

I have the word **sickness**.

Who has the word that identifies a **state of** being slightly wet?

I have the suffix **-ness**.

Who has the word that identifies a region of the untamed world that is covered in forests?

I have the word **dampness**.

Who has the word that identifies a **state of** imaginative thinking?

I have the word **wilderness**.

Who has the word that identifies silliness or a lack of thinking?

I have the word **cleverness**.

Who has the first card?

More Prefixes and Suffixes © 2007 Creative Teaching Press

Vocabulary Quiz: -ness

Shade in the bubble for the correct word.

1 Tammy's poor judgment in making choices can be described as what?
    Ⓐ **boldness**   Ⓑ **foolishness**   Ⓒ **fondness**   Ⓓ **cleverness**

2 Jamie seemed to be spending a great deal of time at the doctor. Why?
    Ⓐ **sickness**   Ⓑ **sadness**   Ⓒ **dampness**   Ⓓ **boldness**

3 The new hit game show rewards people for unique ideas that show thinking and creativity. What is rewarded?
    Ⓐ **wilderness**   Ⓑ **foolishness**   Ⓒ **fondness**   Ⓓ **cleverness**

4 Matt loves to take Jill camping where it is untamed and untouched by humans. Where do they go?
    Ⓐ **fondness**   Ⓑ **wilderness**   Ⓒ **boldness**   Ⓓ **sadness**

5 There are many reality shows on television that reward players who have which brave trait?
    Ⓐ **cleverness**   Ⓑ **fondness**   Ⓒ **boldness**   Ⓓ **foolishness**

6 Pat has a crystal collection. She loves adding new crystal figures to her display. How could you describe Pat's love of crystal figures?
    Ⓐ **boldness**   Ⓑ **sadness**   Ⓒ **cleverness**   Ⓓ **fondness**

7 What might you feel in the air when walking outside on a cool spring morning?
    Ⓐ **dampness**   Ⓑ **wilderness**   Ⓒ **foolishness**   Ⓓ **boldness**

8 She was not happy. What feeling did she have?
    Ⓐ **cleverness**   Ⓑ **boldness**   Ⓒ **sadness**   Ⓓ **sickness**

Write the correct form of the word on the line so the sentence makes sense and is grammatically correct.

9 The child star on the hit television show was admired for his _____ and wit.

10 When jogging in the morning, Jim feels _____ in the air.

11 Max has a _____ for airplanes and cars.

12 When _____ is seen in the classroom, it is often punished.

13 If you would like to treat the _____ of a person, then you might want to become a doctor someday.

14 Her _____ was rewarded when she won the Olympic medal for sledding.

15 Many endangered species live in the _____, which explains why it must be protected.

Review Test: -less and -ness

Shade in the bubble for the correct word.

1. The seagull dropped the clam on a rock to crack it open and eat the meat inside. The seagull used what?
   Ⓐ **meaningless**   Ⓑ **cleverness**   Ⓒ **fondness**   Ⓓ **helpless**

2. Patricia was tired of sitting in the chair all morning working at the computer. She kept tapping her fingers, wiggling her toes, and getting up to walk around. What was she?
   Ⓐ **restless**   Ⓑ **sickness**   Ⓒ **painless**   Ⓓ **boldness**

3. The original documents of our first presidents could never be replaced. Therefore, what are they?
   Ⓐ **meaningless**   Ⓑ **foolishness**   Ⓒ **fondness**   Ⓓ **priceless**

4. Anything that seems silly could be described as this.
   Ⓐ **foolishness**   Ⓑ **sickness**   Ⓒ **helpless**   Ⓓ **boldness**

5. George was unable to check e-mail on his computer during the thunderstorm because the power went out. What was his computer?
   Ⓐ **painless**   Ⓑ **sickness**   Ⓒ **boldness**   Ⓓ **useless**

6. The city had plans to build several new shelters for people living on the streets. These people could be described as this.
   Ⓐ **sickness**   Ⓑ **homeless**   Ⓒ **meaningless**   Ⓓ **sadness**

7. If there is something that you like very much, which word could describe your feelings?
   Ⓐ **fondness**   Ⓑ **sickness**   Ⓒ **cleverness**   Ⓓ **meaningless**

8. Krista didn't know what to do. She couldn't protect her kitten! How did she feel?
   Ⓐ **wilderness**   Ⓑ **sadness**   Ⓒ **helpless**   Ⓓ **careless**

9. When you feel this in the air, it often signals that rain is coming soon.
   Ⓐ **dampness**   Ⓑ **sickness**   Ⓒ **restless**   Ⓓ **boldness**

10. You have many words spelled incorrectly in your writing. What were you?
    Ⓐ **meaningless**   Ⓑ **boldness**   Ⓒ **useless**   Ⓓ **careless**

11. You are so brave and daring to try water skiing for the first time. What do you have?
    Ⓐ **fondness**   Ⓑ **priceless**   Ⓒ **boldness**   Ⓓ **cleverness**

12. When many people are unhappy, you can feel this in the air.
    Ⓐ **foolishness**   Ⓑ **sadness**   Ⓒ **fondness**   Ⓓ **useless**

13. Trevor didn't want his life to be without a purpose so he became a teacher. He didn't want his life to be what?
    Ⓐ **meaningless**   Ⓑ **priceless**   Ⓒ **fondness**   Ⓓ **sickness**

14. Solve the analogy. *useless : useful : : _____ : careful*

15. Solve the analogy. *meaningless : meaningful : : _____ : painful*

More Prefixes and Suffixes © 2007 Creative Teaching Press

Word List: -ist

-ist	a person who

Vocabulary	**Definitions**
art**ist** (n)	**a person who** uses imagination, talent, and skill to create works such as paintings, sculptures, and illustrations
dent**ist** (n)	**a person who** takes care of teeth; a doctor who is trained in dental care
final**ist** (n)	**a person who** makes it to the last round of a competition
journal**ist** (n)	**a person who** writes; a writer
natural**ist** (n)	**a person who** loves nature and tries to protect it; **a person who** has specialized knowledge of animals, plants, or nature
optim**ist** (n)	**a person who** sees the positive side of things; a positive person
pessim**ist** (n)	**a person who** sees the negative side of things; a negative person
special**ist** (n)	**a person who** is highly trained in one area; an expert

Vocabulary Sort: -ist

Cut apart the words and definitions. Match each word to its definition. Check your answers by referring to the word list.

journal**ist**	dent**ist**	pessim**ist**	art**ist**
optim**ist**	special**ist**	final**ist**	natural**ist**

a person who loves nature and tries to protect it; **a person who** has specialized knowledge of animals, plants, or nature	**a person who** is highly trained in one area; an expert
a person who uses imagination, talent, and skill to create works such as paintings, sculptures, and illustrations	**a person who** takes care of teeth; a doctor who is trained in dental care
a person who sees the positive side of things; a positive person	**a person who** sees the negative side of things; a negative person
a person who writes; a writer	**a person who** makes it to the last round of a competition

Application and Practice: -ist

Sentence Fill-ins

Complete each sentence with the correct
word. Use each word only once.

| finalist | naturalist | dentist | pessimist |
| artist | specialist | optimist | journalist |

1 An _____ is a person who is talented and creative with paints, pottery, or drawing.

2 Justine was one of three people left in the competition. She was a _____.

3 Even when times are tough, Mario is laughing and joking. He is an _____.

4 A _____ is a person who will help you with a toothache.

5 Eva writes for the newspaper that you see in most grocery stores. She is a _____.

6 A _____ is the kind of person who makes you feel gloomy because he or she never has anything good to say.

7 A podiatrist is a _____ because he or she is a highly trained foot doctor.

8 Aiko was born loving animals and all things in nature. She is a _____.

Crossword Puzzle

Write the word that matches each clue to complete the puzzle.

Across

5. a person who is trained to care for teeth
6. a person who loves nature
7. an expert
8. a person who uses his creativity to create things out of paint

Down

1. a positive person
2. a writer
3. a person who makes negative comments
4. a person who makes it to the last stage of a competition

Read-Around Review: -ist

I have the first card.

Who has the name of **a person who** is highly trained in what he or she does?

I have the word **finalist**.

Who has the suffix that means **a person who**?

I have the word **specialist**.

Who has the name of **a person who** must be good at writing in order to do his or her job?

I have the suffix **-ist**.

Who has the name of **a person who** loves taking care of animals, trees, or anything else in the environment?

I have the word **journalist**.

Who has the name of **a person who** is a doctor specializing in the care of teeth and gums?

I have the word **naturalist**.

Who has the name of **a person who** always seems to have a positive attitude?

I have the word **dentist**.

Who has the name of **a person who** seems to always have something negative to say?

I have the word **optimist**.

Who has the name of **a person who** is talented with paint, clay, drawing, or even writing?

I have the word **pessimist**.

Who has the name of **a person who** is among the last in a competition?

I have the word **artist**.

Who has the first card?

Name _____   Date _____

Vocabulary Quiz: -ist

Shade in the bubble for the correct word.

1 Out of 20,000 people who tried out for the show, Ann was one of the last three on the stage. What was she?
Ⓐ dentist   Ⓑ finalist   Ⓒ journalist   Ⓓ pessimist

2 Doesn't he have anything good to say about the trip he's about to take? He is such a what?
Ⓐ optimist   Ⓑ specialist   Ⓒ pessimist   Ⓓ finalist

3 When Amber hurt her eye, she was sent to an ophthalmologist named Dr. Patel. He's an expert at eye care. What is he?
Ⓐ specialist   Ⓑ naturalist   Ⓒ finalist   Ⓓ optimist

4 This is a word that often describes people who dedicate their lives to caring for the earth.
Ⓐ optimist   Ⓑ journalist   Ⓒ specialist   Ⓓ naturalist

5 This kind of doctor takes care of your teeth. What title does the doctor have?
Ⓐ dentist   Ⓑ naturalist   Ⓒ optimist   Ⓓ pessimist

6 Do you enjoy writing? You might want to become one of these some day.
Ⓐ naturalist   Ⓑ pessimist   Ⓒ journalist   Ⓓ optimist

7 He makes bowls, vases, and plates out of clay and sells them at the festival. What is his profession?
Ⓐ optimist   Ⓑ artist   Ⓒ finalist   Ⓓ dentist

8 Olivia is always looking on the bright side. She doesn't worry or have negative thoughts at all. What is she?
Ⓐ pessimist   Ⓑ specialist   Ⓒ journalist   Ⓓ optimist

Write the correct form of the word on the line so the sentence makes sense and is grammatically correct.

9 If you talk like a _____, then you probably won't have many friends.

10 The latest painting by the _____ is hanging in the window of the gallery.

11 She went to the manicurist who is a _____ at taking care of fingernails.

12 The _____ interviewed the man about why his company was so successful. The interview appeared in the newspaper the next day.

13 Jane Goodall is a famous _____ who has dedicated her life to caring for chimps and jungles of the world.

14 I can't believe Jack is a _____ in the National Spelling Bee! He might win!

15 Denysia has many friends because she is so positive. She's a fine example of an _____.

More Prefixes and Suffixes © 2007 Creative Teaching Press

Word List: -ish

-ish	somewhat, related to, having the characteristic of

Vocabulary	Definitions
child**ish** (adj)	simple; immature; **related to** a younger person's behavior
fool**ish** (adj)	silly; **somewhat** ridiculous; unwise
lav**ish** (adj)	**having characteristics of** extravagance; fancy; full of luxuries
peev**ish** (adj)	**having the characteristic of** a sour mood or temperament
sheep**ish** (adj)	**having characteristics of** meekness or timidity; embarrassed
slugg**ish** (adj)	slow; lacking energy; **somewhat** inactive
squeam**ish** (adj)	easily sickened; easily disgusted; easily shocked; **somewhat** weak or fearful
styl**ish** (adj)	fashionable; **related to** the current fashion trends; having good taste in clothing

Vocabulary Sort:-ish

Cut apart the words and definitions. Match each word to its definition. Check your answers by referring to the word list.

foolish	peevish	lavish	sluggish
stylish	childish	sheepish	squeamish

simple; immature; **related to** a younger person's behavior	easily sickened; easily disgusted; easily shocked; **somewhat** weak or fearful
fashionable; **related to** the current fashion trends; having good taste in clothing	**having characteristics of** meekness or timidity; embarrassed
having the characteristic of a sour mood or temperament	silly; **somewhat** ridiculous; unwise
slow; lacking energy; **somewhat** inactive	**having characteristics of** extravagance; fancy; full of luxuries

More Prefixes and Suffixes © 2007 Creative Teaching Press

Application and Practice: -ish

Sentence Fill-ins ·

Complete each sentence with the correct word. Use each word only once.

peevish	sluggish	childish	squeamish
sheepish	stylish	lavish	foolish

1 After eating a big meal, Betty was feeling _____ and ready for a nap.

2 It was a _____ decision to ride the skateboard without a helmet.

3 What a _____ party! There were gifts, treats, and decorations everywhere!

4 She couldn't even watch the kids on the roller coaster. Just looking at it made her feel _____.

5 The neighbors thought that Mr. Boore was a _____ man because he never stopped to say hello!

6 I love your new hat! It's so _____!

7 She wore a _____ grin on her face when people looked at her on stage.

8 Jamison's behavior was so _____ that he was sent to the principal's office.

Crossword Puzzle ·

Write the word that matches each clue to complete the puzzle.

Across

2. immature; related to a younger person's behavior
5. fancy; extravagant
6. having a sour mood or temper
7. silly; unwise
8. easily sickened; somewhat weak or fearful

Down

1. fashionable; having good taste in clothing
3. shy; embarrassed; self-conscious
4. slow; lacking energy

Read-Around Review: -ish

I have the first card.

Who has the word that **relates to** a fancy and extravagant meal or event?

I have the word **sheepish**.

Who has the word that describes a person who has the **characteristic of** having a bad temperament?

I have the word **lavish**.

Who has the word that describes an outfit that is **somewhat** in fashion and looks nice on a person?

I have the word **peevish**.

Who has the word that is **related to** how you might feel if you lack energy and just want to sit down?

I have the word **stylish**.

Who has the word that describes **somewhat** immature behavior that you would expect from a much younger child?

I have the word **sluggish**.

Who has the word that describes a behavior that is **somewhat** silly and unwise?

I have the word **childish**.

Who has the word that describes how you might feel if you saw someone eating worms?

I have the word **foolish**.

Who has the suffix that means **somewhat**, **related to**, or **having the characteristic of**?

I have the word **squeamish**.

Who has the word that describes a person who is **somewhat** shy and embarrassed?

I have the suffix **-ish**.

Who has the first card?

Name _____   Date _____

Vocabulary Quiz: -ish

Shade in the bubble for the correct word.

1 Todd is terrified of bugs. If he sees one near him he starts to feel sick to his stomach. What is he?
    Ⓐ **squeamish**   Ⓑ **sluggish**   Ⓒ **childish**   Ⓓ **sheepish**

2 When it comes to hearing compliments about her artwork, Alex gets timid or _____.
    Ⓐ **stylish**   Ⓑ **squeamish**   Ⓒ **lavish**   Ⓓ **sheepish**

3 Vin seems always to be in a bad mood. People see him as _____.
    Ⓐ **lavish**   Ⓑ **foolish**   Ⓒ **peevish**   Ⓓ **sluggish**

4 The decorations look very professional. What an incredible hotel! What is this hotel?
    Ⓐ **foolish**   Ⓑ **lavish**   Ⓒ **squeamish**   Ⓓ **childish**

5 Even though she was healthy again, Ria still didn't have very much energy. She was feeling _____.
    Ⓐ **sluggish**   Ⓑ **squeamish**   Ⓒ **stylish**   Ⓓ **peevish**

6 It was an unwise choice for her to walk outside in the cold weather with wet hair. What was her choice?
    Ⓐ **lavish**   Ⓑ **sheepish**   Ⓒ **sluggish**   Ⓓ **foolish**

7 I couldn't believe it when I saw the ten-year-old throwing a fit! What kind of behavior was this?
    Ⓐ **lavish**   Ⓑ **sluggish**   Ⓒ **childish**   Ⓓ **stylish**

8 Phuoug learned how to knit so she could make scarves for her friends. They all looked so great! What are the scarves?
    Ⓐ **stylish**   Ⓑ **childish**   Ⓒ **foolish**   Ⓓ **peevish**

Write the correct form of the word on the line so the sentence makes sense and is grammatically correct.

9 After running five miles, Tom was feeling a bit _____. He decided to walk the rest of the way home.

10 Chloé was _____ when she said she wouldn't share her crackers with her sister.

11 Ronald wore a _____ tie with his suit to the awards banquet.

12 Officer Lee had a _____ grin on his face as he accepted the Medal of Honor because he was not used to being in the spotlight.

13 Did you know that some people feel _____ at the sight of raw fish?

14 Darian made a _____ choice by walking barefoot because she stepped on a piece of glass!

15 Al's _____ behavior got him kicked out of the fancy restaurant.

More Prefixes and Suffixes © 2007 Creative Teaching Press

Review Test: -ist and -ish

Shade in the bubble for the correct word.

1 What kind of person always makes you feel like you will succeed?
    Ⓐ **pessimist**   Ⓑ **childish**   Ⓒ **lavish**   Ⓓ **optimist**

2 Which word describes how you might feel if you just don't have as much energy as usual?
    Ⓐ **sluggish**   Ⓑ **squeamish**   Ⓒ **childish**   Ⓓ **sheepish**

3 If you would like to take care of the animals and earth, what might you become someday?
    Ⓐ **dentist**   Ⓑ **naturalist**   Ⓒ **artist**   Ⓓ **pessimist**

4 People who are this often have few friends.
    Ⓐ **peevish**   Ⓑ **squeamish**   Ⓒ **lavish**   Ⓓ **stylish**

5 This person said that I need a root canal!
    Ⓐ **artist**   Ⓑ **finalist**   Ⓒ **dentist**   Ⓓ **optimist**

6 This person often uses color to create formations of his own design.
    Ⓐ **finalist**   Ⓑ **specialist**   Ⓒ **artist**   Ⓓ **naturalist**

7 Do you like the way this restaurant is decorated? If you think it's too fancy, you may think it is this.
    Ⓐ **lavish**   Ⓑ **sheepish**   Ⓒ **childish**   Ⓓ **squeamish**

8 The Writer's Workshop Competition has selected the best three writers in the county. What are they?
    Ⓐ **artists**   Ⓑ **specialists**   Ⓒ **pessimists**   Ⓓ **finalists**

9 Mrs. Rose was getting gray hair, so she went to a hair stylist who is an expert in hair coloring. An expert can also be called this.
    Ⓐ **finalist**   Ⓑ **artist**   Ⓒ **journalist**   Ⓓ **specialist**

10 Rodney was unwise when he sold his car for less than it was worth. What was he?
    Ⓐ **squeamish**   Ⓑ **peevish**   Ⓒ **foolish**   Ⓓ **sheepish**

11 If you act like this in a restaurant, you'll probably get in trouble for your behavior.
    Ⓐ **childish**   Ⓑ **squeamish**   Ⓒ **sheepish**   Ⓓ **lavish**

12 I can't volunteer at the hospital with you. I get sick at the sight of blood. What am I?
    Ⓐ **peevish**   Ⓑ **squeamish**   Ⓒ **childish**   Ⓓ **sheepish**

13 Solve the analogy. *fashionable :* _____ *:: considerate : thoughtful*

14 Solve the analogy. *optimist : positive ::* _____ *: negative*

15 Solve the analogy. *scientist : researches ::* _____ *: writes*

Word List: -ful

-ful	full of, characterized by

Vocabulary	Definitions
blissful (adj)	**full of** happiness; joyful
bountiful (adj)	**characterized by** having a great deal of something; abundant; plentiful
cheerful (adj)	**full of** good spirits
doubtful (adj)	uncertain; **full of** suspicion
forgetful (adj)	**full of** neglect; **characterized by** being unable to remember
harmful (adj)	**full of** danger; unsafe
meaningful (adj)	**full of** purpose; worthy
successful (adj)	**characterized by** a favorable outcome

Vocabulary Sort: -ful

Cut apart the words and definitions. Match each word to its definition. Check your answers by referring to the word list.

meaning**ful**	cheer**ful**	harm**ful**	doubt**ful**
success**ful**	bliss**ful**	forget**ful**	bounti**ful**

full of neglect; **characterized by** being unable to remember	**characterized by** a favorable outcome
uncertain; **full of** suspicion	**characterized by** having a great deal of something; abundant; plentiful
full of purpose; worthy	**full of** good spirits
full of happiness; joyful	**full of** danger; unsafe

Name _____ Date _____

Application and Practice: -ful

Matching Clues to Vocabulary

Write the word that matches each clue.
Use each word only once.

| forgetful | blissful | successful | harmful |
| bountiful | cheerful | meaningful | doubtful |

1 _____ This word is often on directions for medications to make sure that only the correct amount is taken.

2 _____ Shawna's goal was to graduate from college. Last June, she did. What was she?

3 _____ Owen can't figure out why he keeps losing his keys. He can be described as what?

4 _____ Many grapes were growing on the vines. What word describes this grape harvest?

5 _____ Our school secretary always greets the children with a smile. What is she?

6 _____ I'm having a hard time believing that story. I am what?

7 _____ She thought it was simply a beautiful, sunny day. How did she feel?

8 _____ Her job allowed her to care for babies who were born too soon. She helped save them every day. She felt her job was what?

Crossword Puzzle

Write the word that matches each clue to complete the puzzle.

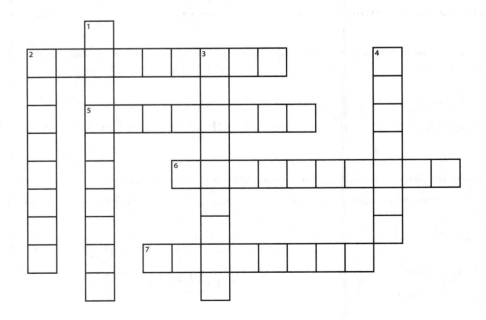

Across
2. abundance; having a great deal of something
5. full of good spirits
6. worthy; has purpose
7. unsure; uncertain; questioning the information

Down
1. something desired was achieved
2. happy or joyful
3. has difficulty remembering things
4. dangerous

Read-Around Review: -ful

I have the first card.

Who has the word that describes a person who is **full of** good spirits?

I have the suffix **-ful**.

Who has the word that describes a large amount of something?

I have the word **cheerful**.

Who has the word that describes a feeling of uncertainty or suspicion?

I have the word **bountiful**.

Who has the word that describes a person who is **full of** happiness?

I have the word **doubtful**.

Who has the word that describes a person who had a goal that was achieved?

I have the word **blissful**.

Who has the word that **characterizes** a person who often has a hard time remembering things?

I have the word **successful**.

Who has the word that describes something that is **full of** danger?

I have the word **forgetful**.

Who has the word that describes something that is **full of** purpose?

I have the word **harmful**.

Who has the suffix that means **full of** or **characterized by**?

I have the word **meaningful**.

Who has the first card?

More Prefixes and Suffixes © 2007 Creative Teaching Press

Vocabulary Quiz: -ful

Shade in the bubble for the correct word.

1 Jamel had a hard time believing that Emily was going to stop shopping so often. He was what?
Ⓐ **forgetful**   Ⓑ **doubtful**   Ⓒ **harmful**   Ⓓ **successful**

2 I'm thankful because I know that I truly make a difference at work. My work is _____.
Ⓐ **meaningful**   Ⓑ **successful**   Ⓒ **bountiful**   Ⓓ **forgetful**

3 Her garden had more flowers than ever before. What was it?
Ⓐ **bountiful**   Ⓑ **blissful**   Ⓒ **harmful**   Ⓓ **cheerful**

4 Danielle spent years saving money to buy her first house. Finally, she was _____ and moved into her very own home.
Ⓐ **forgetful**   Ⓑ **doubtful**   Ⓒ **successful**   Ⓓ **cheerful**

5 Being out in the sun without sunscreen can be _____ to a person's skin.
Ⓐ **harmful**   Ⓑ **meaningful**   Ⓒ **bountiful**   Ⓓ **doubtful**

6 Yasmin's letter to the editor touched many people with her compassionate views on humanity. Her letter was what?
Ⓐ **cheerful**   Ⓑ **blissful**   Ⓒ **doubtful**   Ⓓ **meaningful**

7 Every morning, Sheila woke up with a smile on her face. She was _____!
Ⓐ **doubtful**   Ⓑ **cheerful**   Ⓒ **meaningful**   Ⓓ **successful**

8 They laughed every minute of the day at the amusement park. What kind of day did they have?
Ⓐ **meaningful**   Ⓑ **doubtful**   Ⓒ **bountiful**   Ⓓ **blissful**

Write the correct form of the word on the line so the sentence makes sense and is grammatically correct.

9 Congratulations! I knew you would be _____! What will your next goal be now?

10 I'm _____ that my ankle will be healed in time for the marathon. It's only two weeks away, and I still can't stand on it.

11 He was so _____ when he went to the grocery store that he started making a list to help him remember what he needed.

12 People who are _____ when meeting others are often well liked.

13 Air pollution is _____ to the health of all living things.

14 What a _____ thing to do! You helped her in so many ways.

15 There was a _____ harvest for the first Thanksgiving.

More Prefixes and Suffixes © 2007 Creative Teaching Press

Word List: -ion

-ion	action, process, state, or condition

Vocabulary	Definitions
affection (n)	the **state** of showing that one cares; fondness
cancellation (n)	the **process** of ending or stopping something
complication (n)	a difficulty; a factor that causes a **state** of trouble
donation (n)	the **process** of giving something to someone else; a gift
excavation (n)	the **process** of digging out and removing; the **action** of exposing to view
exception (n)	something that is not included; the **process** of leaving something out
permission (n)	the **process** of allowing something to happen; consent
translation (n)	the **process** of changing from one language to another

Vocabulary Sort: -ion

Cut apart the words and definitions. Match each word to its definition. Check your answers by referring to the word list.

complica**tion**	translat**ion**	excep**tion**	affec**tion**
permiss**ion**	excavat**ion**	donat**ion**	cancellat**ion**

the **process** of ending or stopping something	something that is not included; the **process** of leaving something out
the **state** of showing that one cares; fondness	the **process** of allowing something to happen; consent
the **process** of digging out and removing; the action of exposing to view	the **process** of changing from one language to another
the **process** of giving something to someone else; a gift	a difficulty; a factor that causes a **state** of trouble

Application and Practice: -ion

Sentence Fill-ins

Complete each sentence with the correct word. Use each word only once.

translation	exception	permission	affection
donation	excavation	cancellation	complication

1. Carina made a _____ to her local animal shelter.

2. Lisa had a _____ after the surgery, so she had to stay in the hospital three more days.

3. "With the _____ of Michael, you may all go out to recess. Michael, you need to finish your homework."

4. My mom gave me _____ to spend the night at my friend's house next weekend.

5. At the _____ site, the paleontologist carefully brushed away the dirt from the bones.

6. Antonio showed _____ to his mother by hugging her every time he saw her.

7. Luckily, there was a _____ at the restaurant. Otherwise, we would have had to eat somewhere else. They were booked all night!

8. Claudia did an excellent job on the _____ of the book from French to English.

Crossword Puzzle

Write the word that matches each clue to complete the puzzle.

Across

1. caring or fondness
3. a problem or difficulty
6. the process of stopping something
7. the process of allowing something to happen
8. the process of changing from one language to another

Down

2. the process of digging out and removing
4. something that is not included
5. a gift

Read-Around Review: -ion

I have the first card.

Who has the word that names a gift that is usually given to a charity or group to help others?

I have the word **translation**.

Who has the word that names what you need to get from your parents when you want to do something?

I have the word **donation**.

Who has the word that names what people show when they are caring to someone else?

I have the word **permission**.

Who has the word that identifies a problem or event that stands in your way for a short time?

I have the word **affection**.

Who has the word that names the **process** of digging and removing dirt to look at fossils?

I have the word **complication**.

Who has the word that names what is made when someone changes the rules for one person?

I have the word **excavation**.

Who has the suffix that means **action**, **process**, **state**, or **condition**?

I have the word **exception**.

Who has the word that identifies the **process** of what a person does when ending a subscription to a magazine?

I have the suffix **-ion**.

Who has the word that describes the **process** of changing something from Spanish to English?

I have the word **cancellation**.

Who has the first card?

More Prefixes and Suffixes © 2007 Creative Teaching Press

Vocabulary Quiz: -ion

Shade in the bubble for the correct word.

1. Hugging, smiling, and helping are all forms of _____, showing you care about someone.
   - Ⓐ **donation**
   - Ⓑ **excavation**
   - Ⓒ **affection**
   - Ⓓ **exception**

2. Changing from one language to another is a skill that all bilingual people learn. What is this process called?
   - Ⓐ **translation**
   - Ⓑ **exception**
   - Ⓒ **permission**
   - Ⓓ **complication**

3. All of the classes at Wilson School have nightly homework. Mrs. Graydon's class is the only one that doesn't have homework on Wednesday nights. What is her class?
   - Ⓐ **permission**
   - Ⓑ **complication**
   - Ⓒ **translation**
   - Ⓓ **exception**

4. Mother, may I please have your _____ to go to the ice cream shop after school?
   - Ⓐ **excavation**
   - Ⓑ **permission**
   - Ⓒ **affection**
   - Ⓓ **cancellation**

5. We don't have cable television anymore. What process did we follow to stop it?
   - Ⓐ **cancellation**
   - Ⓑ **permission**
   - Ⓒ **exception**
   - Ⓓ **complication**

6. Gerald sent in a check for $100.00 to the American Cancer Society fundraiser. It was a _____.
   - Ⓐ **complication**
   - Ⓑ **exception**
   - Ⓒ **donation**
   - Ⓓ **affection**

7. We went to the museum to see dinosaur fossils from the Montana discovery dig site. The fossils came from an _____.
   - Ⓐ **exception**
   - Ⓑ **complication**
   - Ⓒ **translation**
   - Ⓓ **excavation**

8. There was a problem with our plan. We had a what?
   - Ⓐ **exception**
   - Ⓑ **cancellation**
   - Ⓒ **complication**
   - Ⓓ **translation**

Write the correct form of the word on the line so the sentence makes sense and is grammatically correct.

9. Please fill out this _____ form and we will stop sending the newspaper to your house.

10. My dog shows his _____ for me by wagging his tail and licking me.

11. The P.E. teacher made an _____ for Ryan when he had a headache. He didn't have to run three laps around the basketball courts like the rest of us.

12. The archeologist just completed the _____ of the ancient Eygptian pyramids.

13. She had her vacation all planned out. However, there were some unexpected _____. The biggest one was rain!

14. The elementary school was accepting _____ to help pay for their new computer lab.

15. The _____ of the Spanish word *hola* to English is *hello*.

Review Test: -ful and -ion

Shade in the bubble for the correct word.

1. When tragic events occur around the world, what do many people give?
   - Ⓐ **donations**
   - Ⓑ **permission**
   - Ⓒ **exceptions**
   - Ⓓ **translations**

2. Why can't Min remember where she parked her car? This happens all the time! What is Min?
   - Ⓐ **bountiful**
   - Ⓑ **doubtful**
   - Ⓒ **exception**
   - Ⓓ **forgetful**

3. You ask for this when you show respect to your parents.
   - Ⓐ **permission**
   - Ⓑ **exception**
   - Ⓒ **excavation**
   - Ⓓ **complication**

4. Which characteristic describes people who are often in a happy mood?
   - Ⓐ **successful**
   - Ⓑ **meaningful**
   - Ⓒ **cheerful**
   - Ⓓ **doubtful**

5. Emergency room doctors and nurses must be prepared for these when dealing with victims of car accidents because there may be internal injuries.
   - Ⓐ **complications**
   - Ⓑ **excavations**
   - Ⓒ **donations**
   - Ⓓ **cancellations**

6. The busy car repair shop had a _____, which allowed us to get our car fixed on such short notice.
   - Ⓐ **permission**
   - Ⓑ **exception**
   - Ⓒ **cancellation**
   - Ⓓ **excavation**

7. The new Web site lists many ways to make every day purposeful and _____.
   - Ⓐ **exception**
   - Ⓑ **meaningful**
   - Ⓒ **doubtful**
   - Ⓓ **blissful**

8. Victoria was the only person in Room 11 not going on the field trip to the farm. What was she in the class?
   - Ⓐ **excavation**
   - Ⓑ **permission**
   - Ⓒ **translation**
   - Ⓓ **exception**

9. I'm having a hard time believing his story! I am _____.
   - Ⓐ **doubtful**
   - Ⓑ **meaningful**
   - Ⓒ **harmful**
   - Ⓓ **bountiful**

10. If you want this word to describe you in life, then you need to always try your best.
    - Ⓐ **successful**
    - Ⓑ **bountiful**
    - Ⓒ **blissful**
    - Ⓓ **doubtful**

11. Stephanie speaks English but was able to understand the speech in Portuguese. What allowed her to understand the speech in Portuguese?
    - Ⓐ **permission**
    - Ⓑ **excavation**
    - Ⓒ **exception**
    - Ⓓ **translation**

12. "You need a name badge to come into this dig site," remarked Dr. Sue. What kind of place is it?
    - Ⓐ **excavation**
    - Ⓑ **complication**
    - Ⓒ **permission**
    - Ⓓ **exception**

13. The lake has tons of fish! What are the fish?
    - Ⓐ **blissful**
    - Ⓑ **bountiful**
    - Ⓒ **forgetful**
    - Ⓓ **doubtful**

14. Solve the analogy. *sad : happy : : _____ : safe*

15. Solve the analogy. *mean : cruel : : love : _____*

Answer Key

e-, ex-

Matching Clues to Vocabulary (page 9)

1. extinguish
2. exhale
3. eject
4. exceed
5. erupt
6. exclude
7. expand
8. emit

Crossword Puzzle (page 9)

Across
1. exhale
2. emit
4. exceed
5. extinguish

Down
1. exclude
2. eject
3. erupt
4. expand

Vocabulary Quiz (page 11)

1. C
2. D
3. A
4. D
5. B
6. A
7. D
8. B
9. exceeded
10. exclude
11. emit
12. ejected
13. erupt
14. expand
15. exhale

in-

Sentence Fill-ins (page 14)

1. inspire
2. inhale
3. inflate
4. include
5. inject
6. inspect
7. instruct
8. invite

Crossword Puzzle (page 14)

Across
1. inspire
2. include
3. invite
5. inhale
6. instruct

Down
1. inflate
3. inject
4. inspect

Vocabulary Quiz (page 16)

1. B
2. A
3. D
4. C
5. A
6. D
7. C
8. B
9. inspected
10. include
11. inspire
12. inject
13. inhale
14. instruct
15. invite

Review Test: e-, ex-, and in- (page 17)

1. B
2. A
3. C
4. D
5. A
6. B
7. D
8. C
9. A
10. B
11. D
12. C
13. D
14. exhale
15. inflate

non-

Matching Clues to Vocabulary (page 20)

1. nondairy
2. nontoxic
3. nonsense
4. nonprofit
5. nonfiction
6. nonhuman
7. nonfat
8. nonverbal

Crossword Puzzle (page 20)

Across
1. nonverbal
3. nondairy
4. nonfat
5. nonprofit
6. nonhuman

Down
1. nonfiction
2. nonsense
4. nontoxic

Vocabulary Quiz (page 22)

1. D
2. B
3. C
4. A
5. D
6. C
7. A
8. D
9. nonfiction
10. nonsense
11. nonfat
12. nontoxic
13. nonprofit
14. nondairy
15. nonverbal

il-, im-, in-, ir-

Sentence Fill-ins (page 25)

1. illegal
2. irregular
3. incapable
4. irreversible
5. inactive
6. impaired
7. immobile
8. impede

Crossword Puzzle (page 25)

Across
4. impaired
6. irreversible
7. inactive

Down
1. incapable
2. irregular
3. impede
4. immobile
5. illegal

Vocabulary Quiz (page 27)

1. D
2. D
3. A
4. B
5. A
6. D
7. A
8. C
9. incapable
10. irregular
11. immobile
12. irreversible
13. inactive
14. illegal
15. impeded

Review Test: non- and il-, im-, in-, ir- (page 28)

1. D
2. A
3. B
4. C
5. A
6. B
7. B
8. A
9. A
10. C
11. D
12. B
13. B
14. inactive
15. nondairy

Answer Key

pro-

Sentence Fill-ins (page 31)

1. protest
2. projectile
3. proceed
4. prolong
5. promotion
6. probable
7. prospect
8. propel

Crossword Puzzle (page 31)

Across
2. protest
3. proceed
5. prospect
6. propel

Down
1. projectile
2. probable
3. promotion
4. prolong

Vocabulary Quiz (page 33)

1. D
2. C
3. A
4. D
5. A
6. A
7. B
8. A
9. promotion
10. projectile
11. protest
12. probable
13. proceed
14. prospect
15. prolong

retro-, an-, anti-

Sentence Fill-ins (page 36)

1. antacid
2. antonym
3. retroactive
4. antihistamine
5. antidote
6. antibacterial
7. retrospective
8. retrofit

Crossword Puzzle (page 36)

Across
1. antibacterial
3. retrospective
4. antacid
5. retroactive
6. antonym

Down
2. antihistamine
3. retrofit
4. antidote

Vocabulary Quiz (page 38)

1. D
2. A
3. B
4. A
5. C
6. A
7. D
8. D
9. retroactive
10. antihistamines
11. antidote
12. antibacterial
13. antacid
14. antonyms
15. retrofit

Review Test: pro- and retro-, an-, anti- (page 39)

1. B
2. D
3. D
4. C
5. A
6. A
7. A
8. B
9. D
10. C
11. B
12. C
13. D
14. B
15. C

ab-

Sentence Fill-ins (page 42)

1. absolve
2. absurd
3. abstain
4. absent
5. absorb
6. abrupt
7. abstract
8. abduct

Crossword Puzzle (page 42)

Across
1. absolve
3. abstract
5. absorb
6. abduct

Down
1. abrupt
2. abstain
3. absent
4. absurd

Vocabulary Quiz (page 44)

1. B
2. D
3. A
4. D
5. B
6. A
7. C
8. A
9. abstract
10. abrupt
11. absorb
12. absolve
13. abstain
14. absurd
15. absent

ad-

Sentence Fill-ins (page 47)

1. adapt
2. adhere
3. adhesive
4. adjacent
5. admission
6. address
7. advance
8. adjourn

Crossword Puzzle (page 47)

Across
1. adapt
4. adhesive
5. address
6. adhere
7. adjourn

Down
1. admission
2. adjacent
3. advance

Vocabulary Quiz (page 49)

1. B
2. D
3. B
4. C
5. C
6. B
7. D
8. A
9. adapt, advance
10. address
11. adjourn
12. adjacent
13. adhesive
14. admission
15. adhere

Review Test: ab- and ad- (page 50)

1. B
2. B
3. A
4. D
5. C
6. A
7. A
8. D
9. A
10. D
11. A
12. A
13. C
14. A
15. B

Answer Key

de-

Matching Clues to Vocabulary (page 53)

1. decline
2. decode
3. decrease
4. decay
5. deduct
6. depress
7. deport
8. dejected

Crossword Puzzle (page 53)

Across
1. deport
2. dejected
4. decline
5. decay
6. decode

Down
1. deduct
3. depress
4. decrease

Vocabulary Quiz (page 55)

1. D
2. B
3. A
4. C
5. A
6. B
7. C
8. A
9. depress
10. dejected
11. deport
12. decay
13. decrease
14. decline
15. deduct

dif-, dis-, dys-

Sentence Fill-ins (page 58)

1. dismiss
2. dispense
3. dysfunctional
4. disconnect
5. disagree
6. disobey
7. differentiate
8. differ

Crossword Puzzle (page 58)

Across
2. dismiss
4. differ
7. dysfunctional

Down
1. differentiate
3. dispense
4. disconnect
5. disobey
6. disagree

Vocabulary Quiz (page 60)

1. A
2. D
3. B
4. C
5. A
6. B
7. D
8. A
9. differ
10. dismissed
11. dispense
12. dysfunctional
13. differentiate
14. disobey
15. disagreed

Review Test: de- and dif-, dis-, dys- (page 61)

1. D
2. B
3. B
4. A
5. D
6. D
7. A
8. C
9. A
10. A
11. D
12. D
13. A
14. C
15. B

equ-, equi-

Matching Clues to Vocabulary (page 64)

1. equiangular
2. equator
3. equivalent
4. equinox
5. equation
6. equilateral
7. equal
8. equate

Crossword Puzzle (page 64)

Across
2. equal
5. equate
8. equiangular

Down
1. equilateral
3. equivalent
4. equator
6. equation
7. equinox

Vocabulary Quiz (page 66)

1. D
2. A
3. C
4. B
5. D
6. A
7. C
8. C
9. equate
10. equation
11. equivalent or equal
12. equilateral, equiangular
13. equal or equivalent
14. Equinox
15. equator

hemi-, semi-

Sentence Fill-ins (page 69)

1. Hemisphere
2. semiannual
3. semiarid
4. semiconscious
5. semiformal
6. semisweet
7. semicircle
8. semiweekly

Crossword Puzzle (page 69)

Across
1. semiarid
2. semiweekly
4. semicircle
5. semisweet
6. hemisphere
7. semiformal

Down
1. semiconscious
3. semiannual

Vocabulary Quiz (page 71)

1. B
2. D
3. C
4. B
5. A
6. D
7. C
8. A
9. semisweet
10. semiweekly
11. Hemispheres
12. semiannual
13. semicircle
14. semiconscious
15. semiformal

Review Test: equ-, equi- and hemi-, semi- (page 72)

1. B
2. D
3. A
4. A
5. D
6. C
7. A
8. D
9. A
10. C
11. A
12. A
13. C
14. C
15. A

Answer Key

cent-, centi-, dec-, deca-

Matching Clues to Vocabulary (page 75)

1. decathlon
2. centipede
3. decimal
4. decagon
5. decade
6. century
7. centennial
8. centimeters

Crossword Puzzle (page 75)

Across
1. decagon
3. century
5. decathlon
6. decade
7. decimal

Down
2. centipede
3. centimeter
4. centennial

Vocabulary Quiz (page 77)

1. B
2. C
3. D
4. A
5. D
6. B
7. C
8. A
9. centipede
10. centimeter
11. Decathlon
12. decagon
13. decades
14. decimal
15. centennial

penta-, oct-, sol-, soli-

Sentence Fill-ins (page 80)

1. pentathlon
2. octopus
3. solitaire
4. octet
5. pentagon
6. octave
7. solitude
8. octagon

Crossword Puzzle (page 80)

Across
1. pentathlon
3. octopus
5. octave
6. octagon
7. octet

Down
1. pentagon
2. solitaire
4. solitude

Vocabulary Quiz (page 82)

1. D
2. A
3. C
4. B
5. A
6. A
7. D
8. C
9. octopus
10. solitaire
11. octet, octave
12. pentathlon
13. solitude
14. octagons
15. pentagon

Review Test: cent-, centi-, dec-, deca- and penta-, oct-, sol-, soli- (page 83)

1. B
2. D
3. A
4. D
5. C
6. B
7. B
8. A
9. D
10. C
11. A
12. pentagon
13. ten
14. decagon
15. octagon

multi-

Matching Clues to Vocabulary (page 86)

1. multiuse
2. multitude
3. multiply
4. multivitamin
5. multilingual
6. multicultural
7. multilateral
8. multimedia

Crossword Puzzle (page 86)

Across
2. multicultural
3. multimedia
5. multivitamin
6. multitude
7. multilateral

Down
1. multilingual
2. multiuse
4. multiply

Vocabulary Quiz (page 88)

1. D
2. D
3. A
4. B
5. C
6. D
7. C
8. B
9. multiply
10. multitude
11. multiuse
12. multivitamin
13. multilingual
14. multicultural
15. multimedia

auto-, self-

Sentence Fill-ins (page 91)

1. autobiography
2. autocrat
3. autograph
4. self-sufficient
5. automatic
6. autonomy
7. self-confident
8. automobile

Crossword Puzzle (page 91)

Across
4. self-sufficient
5. autonomy
7. autograph
8. automobile

Down
1. self-confident
2. autobiography
3. automatic
6. autocrat

Vocabulary Quiz (page 93)

1. C
2. A
3. D
4. A
5. A
6. D
7. A
8. B
9. self-sufficient
10. automobile
11. automatic
12. autobiography
13. self-confident
14. autonomy
15. autograph

Review Test: multi- and auto-, self- (page 94)

1. D
2. B
3. C
4. A
5. B
6. D
7. D
8. C
9. A
10. C
11. D
12. B
13. A
14. multilateral
15. autobiography

Answer Key

micro-

Matching Clues to Vocabulary (page 97)

1. microphone
2. microscope
3. microwave
4. microfilm
5. microchip
6. microcosm
7. microscopic
8. microbiology

Crossword Puzzle (page 97)

Across
3. microchip
4. microphone
5. microbiology
6. microscope

Down
1. microscopic
2. microwave
3. microcosm
4. microfilm

Vocabulary Quiz (page 99)

1. D
2. A
3. C
4. B
5. A
6. D
7. A
8. C
9. microbiology
10. microchip
11. microphone
12. microscopes
13. microfilm
14. microwave
15. microscopic

mega-, megal-, megalo-

Sentence Fill-ins (page 102)

1. megabytes
2. megalomania
3. megavitamin
4. megaphone
5. megalosaurus
6. megalopolis
7. megastar
8. megalith

Crossword Puzzle (page 102)

Across
5. megalomania
6. megalith
7. megastar
8. megaphone

Down
1. megalosaur
2. megavitamin
3. megalopolis
4. megabyte

Vocabulary Quiz (page 104)

1. D
2. A
3. D
4. A
5. B
6. C
7. A
8. B
9. megaphone
10. megalosaur
11. megastar
12. megavitamins
13. megabytes
14. megalomaniac
15. megalopolis

Review Test: micro- and mega-, megal-, megalo- (page 105)

1. B
2. D
3. C
4. A
5. A
6. D
7. D
8. A
9. B
10. D
11. C
12. B
13. A
14. megabytes
15. microscope

-less

Matching Clues to Vocabulary (page 108)

1. homeless
2. priceless
3. restless
4. helpless
5. useless
6. meaningless
7. careless
8. painless

Crossword Puzzle (page 108)

Across
4. priceless
5. meaningless
6. helpless
7. useless

Down
1. careless
2. restless
3. homeless
4. painless

Vocabulary Quiz (page 110)

1. C
2. A
3. B
4. D
5. B
6. A
7. D
8. C
9. meaningless
10. homeless
11. helpless
12. careless
13. priceless
14. painless
15. restless

-ness

Sentence Fill-ins (page 113)

1. wilderness
2. fondness
3. foolishness
4. dampness
5. cleverness
6. boldness
7. sadness
8. sickness

Crossword Puzzle (page 113)

Across
4. foolishness
6. cleverness
7. sadness
8. dampness

Down
1. fondness
2. boldness
3. wilderness
5. sickness

Vocabulary Quiz (page 115)

1. B
2. A
3. D
4. B
5. C
6. D
7. A
8. C
9. cleverness
10. dampness
11. fondness
12. foolishness
13. sickness
14. boldness
15. wilderness

Review Test: -less and -ness (page 116)

1. B
2. A
3. D
4. A
5. D
6. B
7. A
8. C
9. A
10. D
11. C
12. B
13. A
14. careless
15. painless

Answer Key

-ist

Sentence Fill-ins (page 119)

1. artist
2. finalist
3. optimist
4. dentist
5. journalist
6. pessimist
7. specialist
8. naturalist

Crossword Puzzle (page 119)

Across
5. dentist
6. naturalist
7. specialist
8. artist

Down
1. optimist
2. journalist
3. pessimist
4. finalist

Vocabulary Quiz (page 121)

1. B
2. C
3. A
4. D
5. A
6. C
7. B
8. D
9. pessimist
10. artist
11. specialist
12. journalist
13. naturalist
14. finalist
15. optimist

-ish

Sentence Fill-ins (page 124)

1. sluggish
2. foolish
3. lavish
4. squeamish
5. peevish
6. stylish
7. sheepish
8. childish

Crossword Puzzle (page 124)

Across
2. childish
5. lavish
6. peevish
7. foolish
8. squeamish

Down
1. stylish
3. sheepish
4. sluggish

Vocabulary Quiz (page 126)

1. A
2. D
3. C
4. B
5. A
6. D
7. C
8. A
9. sluggish
10. peevish
11. stylish
12. sheepish
13. squeamish
14. foolish
15. childish

Review Test: -ist and -ish (page 127)

1. D
2. A
3. B
4. A
5. C
6. C
7. A
8. D
9. D
10. C
11. A
12. B
13. stylish
14. pessimist
15. journalist

-ful

Matching Clues to Vocabulary (page 130)

1. harmful
2. successful
3. forgetful
4. bountiful
5. cheerful
6. doubtful
7. blissful
8. meaningful

Crossword Puzzle (page 130)

Across
2. bountiful
5. cheerful
6. meaningful
7. doubtful

Down
1. successful
2. blissful
3. forgetful
4. harmful

Vocabulary Quiz (page 132)

1. B
2. A
3. A
4. C
5. A
6. D
7. B
8. D
9. successful
10. doubtful
11. forgetful
12. cheerful
13. harmful
14. meaningful
15. bountiful

-ion

Sentence Fill-ins (page 135)

1. donation
2. complication
3. exception
4. permission
5. excavation
6. affection
7. cancellation
8. translation

Crossword Puzzle (page 135)

Across
1. affection
3. complication
6. cancellation
7. permission
8. translation

Down
2. excavation
4. exception
5. donation

Vocabulary Quiz (page 137)

1. C
2. A
3. D
4. B
5. A
6. C
7. D
8. C
9. cancellation
10. affection
11. exception
12. excavation
13. complications
14. donations
15. translation

Review Test: -ful and -ion (page 138)

1. A
2. D
3. A
4. C
5. A
6. C
7. B
8. D
9. A
10. A
11. D
12. A
13. B
14. harmful
15. affection